CRUEL DEATH, HEARTLESS AFTERMATH

MY FAMILY'S END-OF-LIFE NIGHTMARE, AND HOW TO AVOID IT

A moving memoir of suffering and injustice . . . and an urgent wake-up call.

BARBARA MANCINI

Mechanicsburg, PA USA

Published by Sunbury Press, Inc.
Mechanicsburg, Pennsylvania

www.sunburypress.com

ISBN: 978-1-62006-357-6 (Trade paperback)

Library of Congress Control Number: 2019954314

FIRST SUNBURY PRESS EDITION: November 2019

Product of the United States of America
0 1 1 2 3 5 8 13 21 34 55

Set in Adobe Garamond
Designed by Crystal Devine
Cover by Lawrence Knorr
Cover art by Mary Helen Gregory
Edited by Jennifer Cappello

Continue the Enlightenment!

CONTENTS

Prologue

AT AGE NINETY-THREE, my father, Joe Yourshaw, was a shell of the steely, determined, self-reliant man he used to be. A decorated World War II veteran who survived the Battle of the Bulge, he had escaped the poverty of Pennsylvania's coal country and built his own successful business. Never one to depend on others, he was a self-taught master mechanic who could rebuild a wrecked sports car, replace the transmission in a M-4 tank on the battlefield, or fix a broken-down front-end loader. He had continued to tackle projects well into old age, climbing a ladder onto his roof at age ninety, and single-handedly replacing the entire kitchen floor at the age of ninety-one.

But, advancing age and years of untreated diabetes and cardiovascular disease had finally taken their toll. He struggled to walk and depended on others for help with bathing. Unending fatigue robbed him of the most pleasurable activities of his life, and he was in constant pain.

"I'm tired of living this way. I'm ready to die," he would say. "If you can't enjoy life, what good is it?"

Unlike so many families, we had the difficult discussions about his end-of-life wishes and preferences. Above all else, he wanted to make his own decisions about his end-of-life care and to have those decisions respected. "I want everything possible done so I can stay at home," he said repeatedly. "I do not want any heroic measures, and I absolutely do not want to go to a hospital."

We prepared his advance directive together, and he appointed me his health-care proxy, in case he could no longer make his own decisions. He trusted me to honor his values and wishes. I am a nurse and well-informed about medical care. I thought I knew enough to guide both my parents through this process.

As Dad's condition deteriorated, he enrolled in home-based hospice care, which is supposed to provide comfort as final days approach and smooth the way to a dignified, peaceful death at home.

It was not to be.

A simple act of compassion on my part led my father to a medically intensive, horribly painful death in the hospital—and left me an accused felon. If this could happen to me, it could happen to anyone.

CHAPTER 1

The Fateful Day

All history is the history of unintended consequences.

—T. J. Jackson Lears

IN FEBRUARY 2013, my father was ninety-three and declining quickly, but he was determined to do things his own way. He and Mom were still living on their own in their home of fifty-five years in Pottsville, Pennsylvania. Unsteady on his feet but still able to shuffle slowly along, he refused to use a walker. He had fallen several times recently and took an especially bad fall on the morning of February 6.

Though Mom was ten years younger than Dad, she was considerably smaller, and it took all her strength to help him get up. That night was the worst Dad ever experienced, as I learned in a tearful phone call from Mom. My brother, Jim, had stopped by and tried to help get Dad ready for bed. The chronic pain Dad had endured for several years had escalated so much that he wouldn't allow them to touch him. As they tried to ease a baggy button-down shirt off his shoulders, he cried out, "You're breaking my arms!"

Dad had complained a lot about his pain for a long time, but that kind of wail was very uncharacteristic. He was in so much pain he ended up going to bed fully dressed. I was at home in Philadelphia, two hours away. I asked Mom to give him his morphine (a low dose that I knew was unlikely to provide any relief) and assured her I would be there early in the morning. Although Dad was under home hospice care, we never even thought about calling the hospice. I had called a week earlier to request stronger pain medicine for Dad but got nowhere with them. I wasn't going to waste time arguing with them again. It seemed as if we were on our own.

I arrived the next morning in Pottsville. It was a bone-chilling February day, the landscape a bleak scene of brown leafless trees, streets lined with shrinking piles of dirty snow, and overcast gray skies. At the front porch, I slowly turned the doorknob and tiptoed into the living room. The blinds were drawn, and the darkened room was quiet except for the rhythmic ticking of the wall clock. As my eyes adjusted to the dim light, I could see Dad asleep on the hospital bed, a sheet and blanket draping the hills and valleys of his bony frame.

To talk without disturbing Dad, Mom and I sat at the kitchen table. As she sipped her coffee, her fingers curling around the warm mug emblazoned with *World's Best Grandma*, I told her to go ahead and take some time for herself. I planned to stay all day, to give her a much-needed break and get Dad more comfortable.

In the living room were the familiar hallmarks from my childhood: the wool carpeting Dad had laid so many years earlier, worn thin by the parade of feet from a family of six; the drum-style wooden end tables Dad had bought at an estate sale and polished; the hand-painted lamps that adorned them; my maternal grandmother's ancient foot-pedal organ with its elegant carvings; and at the opposite end, the hulking black player-piano that Dad bought second-hand, brought home disassembled, and reassembled by himself in the living room. I remembered Dad closing off the door to the dining room while we worked on our piano lessons, trying to shield his ears from our unartful attempts at making music.

Everywhere there was evidence of his tinkering with commonplace things to make them more convenient or comfortable. On the window-mounted air conditioner, he'd fastened a plastic shield to divert the air and keep it from blowing directly on him or Mom. On the ceiling fan, he'd installed a tiny light bulb at the end of the chain that switches the light on and off, to distinguish it from the chain that controls the fan. The doorbell, instead of ringing "ding-dong," played the opening strain of "Beautiful Dreamer," a fond reminder of how he put his unique, but not always tasteful, stamp on his living space. It seemed strange to see this room with his favorite reclining chair now removed and replaced by a hospital bed.

Eventually, Dad awoke, startled to see me, then broke into a quick smile. As he tried to sit up, he winced and groaned. He insisted he wanted to go to the bathroom, even though he was barely able to get up, even with my help. Fearful he might fall again, I was able to persuade him to use the bedside commode—something he had steadfastly refused before. His undershorts were wet and smelled of urine, so I helped him put on clean ones. He refused to change the rest of his clothes, and he gingerly lowered himself back into the hospital bed.

"Barb, bring my pain medicine in to me. I can't stand another day like yesterday. And bring me some orange juice," Dad said.

His pain medicine was morphine, a concentrated liquid in a one-fluid ounce plastic vial, about the size of a shot glass. He had been taking a low dose of it at intervals throughout the week, but it wasn't providing any relief. I brought the juice, the morphine, and a measuring syringe. Dad drank the juice and asked for the morphine vial. I have arthritis in both hands, so I handed the vial to him to remove the childproof cap. My mother, who also struggles with arthritic hands, always did the same.

Dad unscrewed the cap, and as I turned to pick up the measuring syringe, he quickly drank what was left of the morphine. I had not checked to see exactly how much was left, but it could have been a very substantial dose.

Was this an attempt to end his life? I don't know. He told me he was in pain, but he never said he intended to end it all. I also don't know if he had any inkling that too much morphine could stop his breathing and kill him.

"Dad," I said, "you just took a *very* large dose of morphine."

Brushing off my concern, he said, "I just want to sleep."

The liquid morphine he took, Roxanol, is a rapid-acting type that has its peak effect in one to two hours. Did he overdose? Was he at risk of dying? We'd soon find out.

I looked at the pale, shriveled skin on Dad's arms; the bony fingers with their knobby joints; his perpetually crooked left index finger; the thin wisps of white hair on a scalp that once was covered with a thick, wavy, dark-brown mat. He seemed so frail, yet he was still the determined and forceful person my father had always been. He had suffered much over the past year, enduring constant pain and steadily losing his independence and dignity.

Dad had made it abundantly clear he never wanted to go to a hospital. He had written advance directives that clearly rejected life-prolonging treatment. He had designated me as his health-care proxy to ensure that his wishes would be honored. I weighed my limited options: Be good to my word and honor Dad's wishes or take some action to treat what may have been a fatal overdose.

Ultimately, I decided that what he did would ease his suffering, and that was what mattered most. I sat next to the bed, held his hand, and we talked, with occasional periods of silence. I wasn't going to admonish him for gulping the morphine, which seemed to me to be impulsive more than calculated. He wanted relief from suffering, that much was clear.

Within minutes, Dad's grimace relaxed, and he began to reminisce. He liked to recount his World War II experiences, and true to form, he spoke of another winter sixty-nine years ago—a winter he would never forget:

> "We got into St. Vith [Belgium] and it was cold as could be. When we moved into the Ardennes it was colder still. The snow was at least three feet deep, then it would change over to freezing rain for a bit, and then overnight everything would freeze up—the tanks, the trucks, everything. I never felt anything that cold. I really hate the cold and snow.
>
> "We were completely surrounded by the Germans. There were frozen bodies in the snow and tanks with entire crews dead inside. I don't understand how I made it out of there alive."

Now, at the opposite end of life, he said, "It's no good getting old. What the hell good is it if you can't do anything? I don't want to be a burden on your mother." He slowly became drowsy over the next hour.

Even though he was lying in this out-of-place hospital bed, he was still in his favorite place in his home—the living room. But the hospital bed represented everything he hated about his life now: his inability to do the things that mattered to him; his loss of control over his life; the physical discomfort; the erosion of his independence; having to look to others for help, including people who were strangers to him. He had said many times that he was ready to die, and I understood why.

About two hours after he took the morphine, a nurse from Hospice of Central Pennsylvania called, asking if she could stop in to check on Dad since he had fallen the day before. I agreed, and she said she would arrive in about fifteen minutes.

The nurse who came was Barbara Cattermole. She had admitted my dad into hospice on his second enrollment a month earlier, but we had never met before. As she entered the living room, I told her I needed to speak to her about something. We walked past my sleeping father into the kitchen.

"My dad asked for his vial of morphine, and when I handed it to him, he drank what was left in it."

"How much was in it?" she asked.

Answering honestly, I said, "I don't know."

With a concerned look on her face, she hurried back into the living room and did an assessment of Dad. He was very drowsy, but he was able to follow her fingers with his eyes when she asked him to. She listened to his heart and lungs, and Dad was breathing easily at a normal rate, sixteen breaths per minute. The mood in the room was still calm and quiet, although I was getting teary-eyed. Dad just looked so small and vulnerable. Cattermole apparently thought Dad took a large enough dose to be fatal, because she asked me if I would permit her to do a Reiki treatment to Dad to "help him pass."

I was vaguely familiar with Reiki; it is a type of therapy that uses hands-on touch to promote healing and emotional well-being by channeling energy from the therapist to the person. I saw no harm in this; Dad was quiet and seemed to be in no distress and was breathing normally. I didn't know if Dad was close to dying at this moment or just very drowsy.

Hovering over Dad, Cattermole calmly and quietly touched his head, shoulders, arms, torso, hips, and legs, then waved her hands over him from head to toe in what are called chakras, or different energy fields. The quiet of the room was broken only by the ticking of the clock on the wall. Dad appeared to be asleep. The whole process took around seven to ten minutes. When she finished the Reiki, Cattermole said, "I'm going to need to be here for a while. I'll have to rearrange my day's appointments."

Even though it was February, and quite cold, Cattermole walked through the kitchen and out the back door to make her call. I stayed in the living room with Dad, sitting quietly next to him while he slept, and dialed Mom's cell phone, hoping to let her know what was happening at home—but there was no answer.

When Cattermole returned, her demeanor changed. "You need to call an ambulance," she declared forcefully. "Your father has to go the hospital. He has to be treated for an overdose."

My mind flashed back to ten years earlier, when my mother-in-law was dying in home hospice care. She had received liberal amounts of morphine, and the family was instructed to give more at the first indication she was in any pain, such as moaning or restlessness. Here, my father finally had some relief from the steadily increasing pain that wracked his body, and she planned to send him to the very treatment he had explicitly rejected.

When I balked, Cattermole insisted that Dad would have to go to the hospital to be treated for an overdose.

I frantically pointed out that this was exactly what Dad did not want. "Why are you doing this?" I demanded.

She snapped, "You know I had to report this!"

"Why? I'm not going to let you take him to the hospital!" Now I was yelling. "He has an advance directive. He absolutely does not want to go to the hospital! He took the morphine because he's in terrible pain—the whole time he's been in hospice, you've never effectively treated it!"

"Morphine's not effective for chronic pain," she retorted.

Stunned, I wondered why in hell he was prescribed something that was ineffective for his pain.

It's possible she meant that Roxanol is ineffective for chronic pain, as it is a short-acting pain reliever, and not a sustained or extended-release medication. Or perhaps she was correct: Maybe morphine was not the appropriate medicine to treat Dad's type of pain. Either way, Cattermole had just admitted that my father's pain was not being properly treated.

"I won't let you take him to the hospital! That's not what he wants, and you know it!"

"My supervisor says he has to go," she snapped.

"Then I want to talk to your supervisor."

Cattermole pulled her cell phone from her bag and punched in the number. She handed her phone to me and I was soon speaking with a person who identified herself as the clinical director, Barbara Woods.

"Why are you saying my father has to go to the hospital?"

"Because he has taken too much medicine and overdosed. He has to go."

"That's bullshit! Your hospice never gave him what he needs for pain. How can you people say you provide comfort in dying? You sure as hell haven't done so for my father!"

"He has to go to the hospital. We are calling 911," Woods insisted.

"I'm not going to let you take him. He was very clear he does not want to go to the hospital. He has a living will. He is refusing all treatment." I was yelling into the phone. "What the hell is wrong with you people! You never treated his pain right to begin with. And now you're going to do this?"

"If you don't call an ambulance, we will!" she retorted.

"Then you better just tear the sheet out of your mission statement that says the dying have the right to be free from pain and have their dignity respected!" I yelled.

"We're calling 911 to take him to the hospital," Woods answered.

With that, I threw the cell phone against the wall, and I yelled at Cattermole, "Get out!"

Clearly flustered, she said nothing, gathered up the phone and left. Never before had I lost my professional cool, even though I dealt with numerous tragic and emergency situations in my career as a nurse. But I wasn't a nurse now. I was a daughter, trying to honor my father's wishes and ensure his comfort and dignity. It was inconceivable that this hospice was so determined to do exactly what my father was adamant that he never wanted.

A few minutes later, the doorbell rang and I heard knocks at the front door. Through the window, I could see two uniformed police officers. From the front picture window, I had seen Cattermole meeting them across the street from the house, where she presumably told them her version of events. Because I felt innocent, I thought the officers would be supportive. I opened the door and Captain Steven Durkin of the Pottsville Bureau of Police asked if they could come in. I agreed. He and the patrol officer saw Dad lying quietly in the bed, seemingly asleep.

Captain Durkin, a middle-aged man with grayish-brown hair, asked me what happened.

"My dad is terminally ill. He's on hospice care and he was in pain. He asked me for his morphine, and I handed it to him. He took his morphine for his pain."

"Well, he has to go to the hospital for treatment," Durkin replied.

"Please don't do that to him! He's suffering and he wants to die. He has a living will, an advance directive. He doesn't want any treatment, and he doesn't want to go to a hospital ever. I am his legal health-care proxy."

"What's he dying from?" Durkin asked.

"From complications of diabetes, high blood pressure, and heart disease," I answered, tears spilling over my cheeks.

At this I noticed a sidelong glance and eye-roll between Durkin and the patrol officer. They obviously didn't believe me. (I have since discovered that many people seem to believe that the only people who qualify for hospice care are those with cancer and AIDS, and it seems like that was the case with the Pottsville police. In fact, in 2013, the year this happened, 63.1% of all hospice admissions were for *non-cancer* diagnoses.[1])

The paramedics arrived next, and as they assembled next to Dad's bed, I pleaded with them: "Please, please, leave my father alone. He

1. https://stateserv.com/wp-content/uploads/Hospice-Care-in-America-2013-Facts-Figures.pdf, p. 7.

doesn't want this. He has advance directives. He absolutely does not want any life-saving treatment. He never, never wants to go to the hospital. He's suffering and he wants to die."

I didn't realize then that those words, said in anguish and distress—"he's suffering and he wants to die"—would be used against me. I never said I gave Dad the morphine *so that* he could die.

"I'm his health-care proxy," I insisted. "I know what he wants, and he absolutely does not want to go to the hospital!"

"Ma'am, you no longer have any say in what happens to your father," Captain Durkin said. "Medics are taking him to the hospital."

The medics moved Dad onto their stretcher, strapped him in, and wheeled him out to the ambulance as I watched, terrified for him and completely helpless to stop them.

Durkin, still inside the house, turned to me and announced, "Ma'am, you're under arrest for assisting a suicide."

"What?! You're *arresting* me?"

All I did was hand Dad his medicine. He made the choice to take what was left in the vial. Dad had ready access to his morphine, was able to walk, and could take his own medicines. How did I assist a suicide?

I pleaded with Durkin to allow me to wait until Mom returned from her errands. He grudgingly agreed. I tried calling Mom what seemed like a hundred times, but, as usual, she did not pick up—she could not hear the ringtone on her phone. In desperation, I called my brother, Jim, who worked nearby, and begged him to come to the house immediately. I called my husband, Joe, to tell him what had happened, and he made hurried arrangements to get to Pottsville. Jim arrived within a few minutes and found me frantic and sobbing. Unable to reach Mom, we waited for what seemed like an eternity for her to come home, even though, in reality, it was only about ten minutes. Walking in the door, shopping bags in hand, she saw the police in her living room, Dad's empty bed, me in a panic, and Jim at my side. As Jim tried to fill her in, she stood immobilized in bewilderment and disbelief.

Mom and Jim watched in shock as the police led me out of the house to the unmarked black police cruiser parked across the street. Unlike a lot of suspects, I was not handcuffed. They steered me into the cold, cramped, dirty back seat. I thought, They've put me in the same place where real criminals sit, like I'm a threat to society. How can this be?

I had never been in trouble before in my life. As a friend later jokingly noted, I never even received detention in high school.

Now I was being led into the police station and standing for a mug shot.

The station room was an open space with a white tile floor, a desk, and a few sparse chairs along a wall. I was not placed in a cell but sat next to Durkin as he pecked at the keyboard to type his report. He turned to me: "Do you want to make a statement?"

"No," I said quietly. He continued typing his report, and Jim walked into the station and sat next to me.

"Jim, how is Mom? You need to go back to the hospital to be with her. She needs you with her."

"No, I'm staying here with you. Toni [Jim's wife/my sister-in-law] is with Mom, so she'll be all right. I'm not leaving you," he insisted.

A few minutes later, my cell phone buzzed, and it was Mom. In a shaky voice, she said, "Barb, I'm at the hospital, and they are asking me to give my consent for them to treat your father. What should I do?"

"Mom, follow his wishes like he discussed. Follow his advance directive," I replied.

Durkin overheard the conversation. "Give me your phone," he commanded. I handed it over, and he told Mom, "Let me talk to the doctor." Durkin identified himself to the ER physician, Dr. Henninger, and told him, "If he dies, it will go much worse for her."

Dr. Henninger relayed that message to Mom, who was forced to make an agonizing choice: honoring her promise to Dad, to whom she had been married for sixty-two years, or helping me. She later told me, "No matter what decision I made, I knew it would hurt either you or your father. I knew he was dying, so I did what I could to help you." Mom never imagined she would have to make such a decision, because we had carefully planned, and we thought everything was covered. Indeed, we had done much more than most people do for end-of-life planning—research shows that fewer than a third of American adults have completed advance directives.[2]

Durkin placed the blame squarely on me. "This is what happens when good people do stupid things," he said. To this day, Mom is still haunted by having to make a decision that pitted the welfare of her husband against that of her daughter.

Durkin went on to complete his criminal complaint. It stated, "Defendant intentionally aided another to commit suicide, and her conduct resulted in such attempted suicide, by providing a substantial amount of Morphine Sulfate the [*sic*] Joseph Yourshaw who drank it with the intent to commit suicide, which is in violation of Section 2505(b) of the PA Crimes Code and a Felony of the 2nd degree." To support the charge, Durkin wrote, "She told me that her father asked her for all his morphine so he could commit suicide and she provided it." This was a flagrant falsehood. As I discuss in Chapter 13, I would later discover that police often lie on arrest reports and in court, a phenomenon so common it has a name: "testilying."

After I declined to give a statement, Durkin said, "You may want to call an attorney. You're going to be taken to a district magistrate for arraignment."

"I have no idea who to call," I said, more to myself than to him. In my state of hysteria, I could hardly think. I had not lived in Pottsville for many decades and was not familiar with the legal landscape, so I contacted the attorney who drew up my parents' wills. I sobbed so much he could barely understand what I was saying. He referred me to an attorney at his office who did criminal defense work. By the time the attorney came on the line, I had managed to calm myself enough to explain that I was under arrest and that I would soon be taken to an arraignment. It was late afternoon, around four-thirty, and Durkin interrupted to tell me we had to hurry to the district justice's office before he left for the day. My newly hired attorney told me it wasn't necessary for him to come to the arraignment, but he offered to do so, and I eagerly accepted.

---

2. https://consumer.healthday.com/senior-citizen-information-31/misc-death-and-dying-news-172/2-of-3-americans-don-t-have-advance-directive-for-end-of-life-724320.html.

Durkin led me back out to the squad car, and I rode in the back seat for the few short blocks to Pottsville District Court for arraignment before Magisterial District Judge James K. Reiley. As a law-abiding citizen, I had no idea what to expect. In Pennsylvania, the minor courts like this one are the remnant of an antiquated and anachronistic system. District judges are not selected for their professional qualifications—they are elected by voters for six-year terms. Most people are surprised to learn that the judges in district courts are not required to be lawyers, or to even have attended college. To run for district judge, candidates need only be twenty-one years old and prove that they've taken a state court system training program. If elected, the judge must complete an initial practicum course and attend thirty-two hours of continuing education a year. The district justice I faced was not an attorney; before he was elected in 1993, he ran a restaurant.

The district justice's office, a converted old storefront with a dirty plate-glass window, was situated on Centre Street, which at one time was the commercial hub of Pottsville. During my childhood, it was bustling with shoppers patronizing places like Pomeroy's Department Store, Raring's and Paramount shoe stores, the 5&10 stores like Kresge's and H. L. Greens. There was a Woolworths's, Freedman's Jewelers, Jennings Market Basket, and the old farmer's market. Back then, the street had several clothing stores, along with stately stone banks and two movie theaters.

The once-vibrant commercial area began a slow death-spiral when a mall opened on the outskirts of town in 1974. Today, Centre Street has a mix of small businesses—a florist, tea shop, thrift shops, pharmacies, a counseling center, a few banks, some physician offices, and a small community theater. With few pedestrians and vacant parking spaces in front of shops, Centre Street is the picture of a struggling town attempting to make a comeback.

Durkin walked me into the dreary building and led me to the back. It was a windowless place enveloped by drab walls and old, dark carpeting, with file boxes piled everywhere. My new attorney was already there, and we spoke briefly about how an arraignment, where the accused is read the crimes they are being charged with, works and what would follow.

It was almost evening, and the district justice office was empty, except for me, Durkin, Jim, and my attorney. I sat at the front table facing the judge's desk, and Justice James Reiley, stout, gray-haired, and clothed in a black robe, entered the room from a back door. He and Durkin smiled and greeted each other with a comfortable familiarity. I wasn't particularly worried that the police captain and the district judge knew each other well. It made sense—Pottsville is a small town with a small police force: as of this writing,[3] twenty-two sworn officers and a police chief; Reiley is the only district justice in Pottsville.

Reiley read the charge against me, as Durkin stood to his right. Reiley then queried me:

"Where do you live?"
"Are you married?"
"Do you have any children?"
"How old are they?"
"Are you employed?"
"Do you rent or own a home?"
"Do you have a mortgage?"

This lasted but a few minutes, and I wept through much of it. He then turned to Durkin and asked, "What do you want to see happen here?" Durkin shrugged his shoulders and said, "It's up to you."

Reiley set my bail at $100,000 unsecured, which meant I did not have to put up any money then, but if I failed to appear in court or comply with bail conditions, I would forfeit the entire $100,000. This meant that our home, which my husband and I worked so hard to save and pay for, could be snatched away from us by the state. I was also required to get fingerprinted and was ordered "not to have any contact with the victim unless supervised continuously."

It was cruelly ironic that the bail conditions described my father as a "victim." He was indeed victimized, but not by me. He was victimized by

---

3. 2019.

a law enforcement agent who overrode my father's carefully considered and legally documented wishes. As a caring daughter who tried to relieve his pain and ensure his wishes were respected, I would now be the target of the full force of the criminal justice system. With Mom's consent for treatment secured, Dad would soon begin enduring the invasive, unwanted medical treatment he'd painstakingly tried to avoid.

CHAPTER 2

"If you can't enjoy your life, what good is it?"

All would live long but none would be old.

—Benjamin Franklin

IF EVER THERE was someone who did not want to be hauled away to a hospital to die, it was my father, Joe Yourshaw. From early in his youth, he learned to take care of himself and not rely on others. In adulthood, he took pride in avoiding the health-care system as much as possible, and for years his good health allowed him to. My father's independence, self-determination, and strong work ethic made him the man he was, but near the end of life, they put him at odds with a culture and health-care system that is focused on delaying death at all costs.

Dad and his eleven siblings had learned to be self-sufficient at a young age because it was necessary for survival. He was the ninth child born to parents who immigrated from eastern Europe. His father, Wasyl Jursza (later anglicized to Charles Yourshaw) and his mother, Maria Zajka, met at a boarding house dance in the anthracite coal mining town of St. Clair in Pennsylvania's Schuylkill County. My grandfather was a coal miner, like many of his fellow immigrants. The work was back-breaking and dangerous, and the wages could not support a family of fourteen. Many times, they were hungry. My grandmother struggled to care for her large family, and she was beset with health problems. She died at the age of thirty-nine, leaving behind a husband who had no way to care for so many children, the youngest of whom was just ten years old. The older children took on many of the child-rearing responsibilities, and they quit school to work or help out at home. Nine years later, my grandfather died of black lung disease, a slow, suffocating death caused by years of inhaling coal dust in the mines. My dad talked about watching his father sit next to a window and put his head outside in a futile attempt to breathe some cool air into his ravaged lungs.

The Yourshaw family's hardscrabble life was the norm for many immigrants who came to work in eastern Pennsylvania's anthracite coal country. The coal barons who owned the land enjoyed enormous wealth created on the backs of poorly paid miners. Fortunately for my father, he had the intelligence, talent, and spunk to make a different life.

Dad was fascinated with cars and engines and often skipped school in favor of spending his time at a local auto repair shop. He taught himself how to take cars and trucks that were totally wrecked and restore them to good working order.

His aptitude for engines and mechanical equipment became vital skills for the US Army in World War II. In 1942, Dad enlisted and was assigned to the 293rd Ordnance Medium Maintenance Company, whose job was to keep M4 and M5 armored tanks in service during combat. He rose through the ranks to tech sergeant and had forty-eight soldiers under him in his platoon. His unit fought in the Battle of the Bulge, the deadliest battle of the war, in Belgium's Ardennes forest. Working in bitter cold, snow, and ice, and facing sustained German artillery fire, his company repaired disabled tanks right on the battlefield, sometimes opening hatches to find entire tank crews dead. His service there earned Dad a Bronze Star.

When World War II ended, Dad started his own business doing plumbing, heating, and electrical contracting. It was fitting that he wanted to be his own boss, and not just because he had a strong independent streak. He felt that he could do it the best, whether it was the mechanical work or running the business side. Dad never bought brand-new equipment. He took pride in finding used versions and restoring them to peak condition. He never hired others to do work he could do himself. When his expanding business needed a place to store heavy equipment, he bought and totally renovated an old building. He poured a cement floor, knocked out a side wall to install a large garage door, put in a hydraulic lift to work on his vehicles, and fenced the surrounding grounds.

At home, he was still at work, doing improvements to our house. When I was eight, he replaced the old coal-burning heating system with a state-of-the-art oil burner. He painted and carpeted the house and remodeled the upper floor so each of his four children had their own separate bedrooms. He wired our rooms into a central intercom so Mom could speak to us from two floors down.

When I was in high school, Dad started a hobby business buying wrecked cars to fix up and re-sell. One of them was an MG Midget that had crashed when it was brand new and was a total loss. Dad restored it to shiny red perfection, and he held on to it for a while just for fun, tooling around the neighborhood in his new "toy," while wearing his tan driving cap. He joked that driving the tiny two-seater felt like he was riding in a roller skate. It was no surprise to any of us that his hobby was yet another form of work.

Even in retirement, he kept busy doing what most people would consider to be work. At age seventy-three, he and Mom became snowbirds, splitting time between Pottsville and Dade City, Florida. The Dade City house was on five acres, with grass that he was constantly mowing. He rebuilt the central air conditioning, installed beautiful arching windows in the family room, cleared out the overgrown landscaping, enclosed an open garage, repaired the swimming pool, re-built the deck around it, and poured a cement driveway over the old gravel drive.

Dad's approach to the health-care system was simple: The less he dealt with it, the better. He had been blessed with good health for most of his life. He went thirty years—from his early fifties to his early eighties—without seeing a doctor.

At age eighty-three, when he started exhibiting symptoms of diabetes—excessive thirst and urination—he shrugged it off. He convinced himself he was thirsty all the time because he worked outside in the heat, and the frequent urination was from drinking a lot to quench his thirst.

Because he repeatedly refused our pleas to get his condition checked, I had to trick him into seeing a doctor about it. One day, I brought a urine test home and just casually asked him to give me a sample to test. He readily agreed, and as I had surmised, the level of sugar in his urine was extremely high, proving he had diabetes.

When I confronted him with this reality, his resistance evaporated. Dad went to the doctor and discovered he had high blood pressure and high cholesterol as well as diabetes. Resigned to the seriousness of these diseases, he thereafter became a model patient: He took his medicines faithfully, tested his blood sugar twice daily, and monitored his blood pressure and pulse daily. He drastically cut the carbohydrates and processed foods in his diet. Each time I visited, he proudly showed me his daily blood sugar and blood pressure readings, which he kept in a small black ledger.

But Dad stubbornly resisted his next major encounter with the healthcare system. At eighty-five years old, he was visiting the Florida house alone. He called Mom and implored her, "I need you to come now!" He had fallen several times and asked her to bring him some crutches. It worried Mom because she had never heard him plead for help like that before. She called me with the news shortly after she had jumped in the car with my brother-in-law and started the long trip to Florida.

Knowing it would take another fifteen hours or so for them to get there, and knowing Dad's high blood pressure and diabetes were big risk factors for a stroke, I called him immediately.

"I fell down a few times and I'm having trouble getting up," he explained. "I'm having trouble walking, and I hurt my knee and shoulder." I repeatedly urged him to call 911 and go to the hospital, but he refused to consider it, saying he'd be fine and would wait for Mom to arrive.

Getting nowhere, I phoned Dad's doctor and asked her to call and try to persuade him to go to a hospital. Though Dad was reluctant, she succeeded where I had failed. I later found out that he had packed a suitcase, called 911, and managed to get out the front door, where he was waiting when the ambulance arrived. Sure enough, the hospital confirmed he'd had a stroke.

Dad was very lucky. His stroke was not life-threatening or disabling, and he spent just a few days in the hospital. But he lost the sense of freedom that came with being fully independent and driving to Florida whenever he felt like it.

Settling back into living in Pottsville year-round, he kept up a steady stream of projects. It was unthinkable to him to call a repairperson for something he could do himself. At the age of ninety, he drove Mom crazy with worry by climbing an extension ladder to patch the roof. By the age of ninety-one, he definitely was slowing down, but he still took on physically-taxing projects. The old linoleum floor in the kitchen was worn and pockmarked, so Dad strapped on knee pads, got down on his hands and knees, and set about prepping the old floor surface. He moved a heavy, five-foot-long radiator and the kitchen appliances, then laid down shiny new vinyl tiles. The project lasted almost a week and left him completely exhausted. It took him weeks to recover.

By this point, it was clear: The many years of untreated diabetes and high blood pressure had exacted considerable damage on Dad's health, particularly on his cardiovascular system and kidneys. He was now fatigued constantly and had generalized body pain along with worsening pain in all his joints. He self-medicated with a lot of Tylenol and ibuprofen. Eventually, minimal exertion made him winded, and personal care, like bathing, exhausted him. Mom tried to help him with such tasks, but—as was his nature—he resisted. For as long as I can remember, Dad was meticulous about his personal hygiene; yet now, he wasn't bathing very much.

A few months later, Mom noticed that Dad was no longer taking his medicines for diabetes, blood pressure, cholesterol, and his prostate, although he was still using plenty of Tylenol and ibuprofen. When Mom asked, he told her, "I'm tired of living this way. I'm ready to die."

I made the trip to Pottsville two days later to talk to him face-to-face about it.

"I'm tired all the time. I hurt everywhere," he told me. "I want to eat whatever I feel like eating. Look, I've lived long enough. I'm just going to let nature take its course. Besides, if you can't enjoy your life, what good is it? I don't want to go to the doctor anymore, I don't want to test my blood, I don't want anything done. That's it."

After much pleading and cajoling, Dad agreed to see his regular physician, Dr. Georgetta Lupold, once more in November 2011. In her notes from the visit, she wrote:

> *"Patient is refusing screenings and treatment. He stopped his meds 4 or 5 weeks ago . . . He tells me he does not want to be a burden on his family. He is tired of having pain all over his body and tired of taking pills. He appears chronically ill and in mild distress. . . . He appears to be oriented and rational although disagreeing with pretty much everything I discussed with him. Does not feel depressed."*

Dad was clearly capable of making his own decisions, and he decided he was done with fighting off the inevitable.

Sometimes when I visited, Dad allowed me to check his blood sugar. Once, it was over 700; another time it was 530—both dangerously high levels. When I showed these numbers to him, he just shrugged his shoulders and smiled. He knew they were too high, and he also knew he had every right to refuse to treat them. How he was still alive, I don't know. In the ER where I worked, anyone with a blood sugar over 700 would be admitted to the intensive care unit.

Although Dad was still alive, it was not a pleasant way to live. He grew weaker and moved ever more slowly, occasionally falling. Now ninety-two years old, he was so exhausted he could no longer drive. He would start to read a magazine article and doze off within minutes, the page unturned, magazine resting in his lap. Unread periodicals piled up in a stack next to his chair. Hoping he wouldn't notice, Mom began removing the ones at the bottom of the pile just to keep the stack manageable.

Dr. Lupold had prescribed a narcotic pain reliever, tramadol, which Dad did take. The tramadol did not help his pain at all, but it made him dizzy and constipated—both common side effects of narcotics. However, he refused to go back to the doctor. He was clear—he wanted no more medical interference. And he was resolute that he never wanted to go to a hospital, saying, "I want everything possible done so I can stay at home."

As time passed and he became frailer, I suggested to Dad that hospice care might help him and Mom both. Dr. Lupold agreed he was eligible, concluding that if his illness took its natural course, he had less than six months to live. She referred us to a hospice in the Pottsville area, Hospice of Central Pennsylvania. Other family members had used hospice care and had good experiences. Based on those recommendations, and what I knew professionally of hospice, it seemed to be the right decision. I had no inkling that having Dad enroll in Hospice of Central Pennsylvania would turn out to be the biggest regret of my life.

CHAPTER 3

Hospice Fail

Just as we do now, our ancestors hoped to die in a familiar place among close friends and family; to be safe and gently cared for in their hour of need; to have their last words heard and treasured.

— Katy Butler, *Knocking on Heaven's Door*

WHEN MY FATHER entered home-based hospice care for the first time, on March 27, 2012, just four days after his ninety-third birthday, he was asked two questions:

"Rate your pain on a scale of 1 to 10"—a standard question asked of patients throughout the health-care system—and "Are you uncomfortable due to pain?"

His answers were completely in keeping with his stoic nature and his resolve to carry on in the face of adversity—but they would make his fate worse.

He refused to rate his pain on the 1 to 10 scale. Mom, trying to be helpful, told the hospice admission nurse that Dad's pain was a 3. Though it is impossible for anyone to know and rate another's pain accurately, Mom's response was recorded in his chart.

When Dad was asked, "Are you uncomfortable due to pain?," the answer recorded in his chart was "comfortable despite pain"—even though the notes also said, "patient describes a constant body ache all over."

I wasn't there for any of the hospice visits, but knowing Dad, I'm certain he never uttered the words, "comfortable despite pain." Yet those three words, often repeated on future entries in his hospice chart and in the meeting notes of the hospice interdisciplinary team, would haunt him throughout his hospice care. They would help send him to the hospital for the painful, invasive, and debilitating treatment he'd carefully sought to avoid.

From the start, Dad's hospice chart clearly noted that his goal was to stay at home and that he did not want anything done to extend his life. He also wanted no hospitalizations—his chart noted he was "adamant" about that. Dad had a living will, a DNR (do not resuscitate) order, and had designated me as his health-care power of attorney—all duly noted in his hospice record.

Dr. Lupold ordered Dad to have a comfort kit for his home hospice care, containing various medications including short-acting liquid morphine (Roxanol), for shorter spikes of pain and/or shortness of breath, and more tramadol[1], the narcotic pill for his chronic pain.

Dad had tried tramadol earlier, but it didn't help and made him feel dizzy, a common side effect of taking narcotics. Morphine is also a narcotic, so this time he chose not to use either of the pain medicines. Instead, he relied only on Tylenol and ibuprofen. It was as if he was saying "I'm tough; I can handle it. I survived the Battle of the Bulge in World War II; I was climbing on my roof at the age of ninety. I'm going to refuse strong painkillers for as long as I can."

But he was paying a real price for his stoicism. He repeatedly told us that he had pain all over. Again and again, his hospice record indicates that he complained of pain. His symptoms, the hospice notes say, were "poorly controlled," yet those same files consistently indicate he was "comfortable despite pain"—a bizarre oxymoron. The very definition[2] of

1. https://www.fda.gov/Drugs/DrugSafety/ucm462997.htm.
2. Pain: "physical suffering or discomfort caused by illness or injury." Google Dictionary. 2019.

pain includes experiencing discomfort. Pain may be "tolerable," but one who experiences pain is not "comfortable."

Perhaps the hospice didn't do more for Dad because the report from each visit included the familiar caveat that he was "comfortable despite pain." Conveniently, those three words would also help shield the hospice from getting poor marks for how badly it managed this key aspect of his care.

The question, "Are you uncomfortable due to pain," was asked as part of "the Comfortable Dying Measure," a voluntary quality control assessment that all hospices used at the time. If the patient answered "yes," the hospice was supposed to provide treatment for the pain, and then in 48 to 72 hours ask the question again. The results helped determine if the hospice was meeting standards for managing pain.

But if the patient indicated no discomfort due to pain, as the hospice contends that my father did, then the hospice is not "managing pain" for the purposes of that quality control measure. Magically, the hospice avoids being evaluated for any pain care it delivers to that patient. Hospice of Central Pennsylvania's verbal sleight-of-hand did not serve my father, but it did help the hospice look better to the outside world.

Dad was not a cheery hospice patient. Active until his early nineties, now he wobbled when he walked, he was in constant pain, and he mourned losing his independence. Having hospice staff come into the house to help him offended his pride and his lifelong sense of self-reliance. And he really didn't like having strangers help him with bathing. The first time hospice aides came to do so, he told them to leave. Only after Mom could no longer get him in and out of the shower did he agree to take help with bathing, and then only occasionally.

Hospice records repeatedly indicate that my father "says he has no quality of life" and what he missed most was "being active and independent." But those words apparently didn't make much of an impression on some of the hospice staff. They did not see my father as a proud, self-reliant man who was trying to hold on to his dignity as death approached; they simply saw him as a problem patient. I would later learn that hospice record entries mentioned his "negative attitude"[3] and said he displayed "his usual grumpiness"[4]—disparaging personal remarks that I, with over thirty years' experience in the health-care field, have never seen on a patient chart.

Dad's condition actually stabilized after a few months. Doctors concluded that his death was not imminent, so he was discharged from hospice care on June 24, 2012, with the offer to re-enroll if his condition worsened. We returned the medicines the hospice had provided, all of them unused—a fact that would later prove significant in the criminal case against me. Yet, if, as the police and prosecution would allege in court, I had been plotting to help my father commit suicide, the big collection of powerful drugs in that kit would have done the job, and we would have kept them.

By autumn, Dad was on the decline again, sleeping most of the day, exhausted all the time, falling more often, and taking more ibuprofen and Tylenol. Come mid-January, it was time to consider hospice again.

We bundled Dad up against the blustery, cold weather and took him back to his doctor's office. In his black winter coat and black fedora, he still looked determined and dignified, despite his frailty. The physician assistant who saw him noted that he did not want to prolong his life, but he was not depressed. With Dr. Lupold gone into retirement, a new doctor, whom Dad had never met, approved his re-enrollment in hospice.

Once again, we were dealing with Hospice of Central Pennsylvania. This time, Dad received no pain medicine at all. Perhaps it was because his records consistently indicated he was, in those fateful words, "comfortable despite pain." Or perhaps they justified withholding pain medicine with this notation: "refuses all medications and has disengaged himself from all medical care." It was certainly true that he refused all medicines that treated his multiple health problems. But his frequent use of Tylenol

3. Hospice of Central Pennsylvania Record of Joseph Yourshaw, entry dated May 9, 2012, p.23.
4. *Id.*, entry dated May 29, 2012, p. 34.

and ibuprofen for pain relief continued unabated. Whatever the reason, for Hospice of Central Pennsylvania, neglecting to provide pain relief was another grave deficiency in my father's care. And doing so without informing my mother or me violated a fundamental principle of hospice: that caregivers will be consulted in the treatment of their loved one.

The hospice did provide one service that seemed to help Dad—a therapeutic massage two weeks after his second hospice enrollment. It didn't wipe out his pain but did make it more bearable. However, massage is expensive, and hospices get paid a fixed amount for each day they have a patient in their care. That lump-sum payment system gives hospices an incentive to skimp on expensive services like massages and pocket the difference.

The massage therapist noted that Dad was in a better frame of mind after the massage, and he said that it felt good. In the hospice record, his plan of care included discussion of palliative massage, but he received it just that one time. There's no evidence the hospice ever tried to discuss with him other medications or ways of treating his pain, even though the notes in his file say, "revisions recommended regularly to control symptoms." Apparently, that entry is the kind of automatic cut-and-paste language used to satisfy inspectors who check hospice records. It certainly did not reflect the care my father received.

When I visited on February 1, Dad had told me how increasingly uncomfortable he was. I called the hospice immediately to ask them to prescribe morphine for Dad's pain. I knew that morphine was a standard part of treatment at end of life; it's used in 90% of such cases.[5] Little did I know that the prosecution would soon use my call as "proof" that I was plotting to help my father get the drugs he needed to try to "commit suicide."

I spoke with Deborah Hornberger, a nurse who served as Dad's hospice team leader.

"I'm sorry, it's not appropriate for your father to have morphine," she told me.

---

5. Ernesto Vignaroli, et al. "Strategic Pain Management: The Identification and Development of the IAHPC Opioid Essential Prescription Package." *Journal of Palliative Medicine*, vol. 15, no. 2, 2012, pp. 186-191.

Astonished, I asked why. After all, my father had received morphine from this same hospice six months earlier, no questions asked.

"Your dad is 'opiate-naïve,'" said Hornberger, who is not a doctor. "He has not used any form of opiate for some time and I believe he will not tolerate it well. A better alternative would be Percocet."

Now, I was truly mystified. Percocet is an opiate. Why was she OK with Percocet and not morphine?

I repeated that my father needed morphine, just as he had been provided before. After some hemming and hawing, she finally said, "All right, I will talk to his doctor about this."

But by the next day, my father still didn't have any pain medicine—something that shocked the hospice nurse who visited him. She immediately called about it, and the morphine finally arrived at eight P.M., a full day and a half after I asked.

The morphine Dad finally received was Roxanol, a concentrated liquid in a one-ounce vial, about the volume of a shot glass. It is a short-acting type of morphine, the same kind he'd received on his first hospice enrollment. But due to Hornberger's intervention, the allowable dose had been cut by more than half, to 2.5 milligrams, and the minimum time between doses had doubled, to four hours. And there was another strange twist: His previous prescription had allowed "titration," meaning the patient can increase the dose if needed. It's a common provision in morphine prescriptions, because the body does build up a tolerance to the drug. But this time, there was no indication he was allowed to increase the dose, if needed.

I thought this limited dosing was very odd. But my area of expertise was emergency nursing, not hospice nursing. I thought they must know what they are doing. I didn't know Hospice of Central Pennsylvania had some mysterious bias against providing doses of morphine that might actually give a patient some pain relief.

When later called to testify against me, Hornberger made that bias clear. She admitted working to override the original prescription written by my father's doctor, telling the court, "I did not feel that it was recommended to go above 2.5mg [of morphine]. At any given time."[6]

6. Transcript of Preliminary Hearing at 100, *Commonwealth of Pa. v. Barbara Joy Mancini*, CR-050-13, (Magis. Ct. Aug. 1, 2013).

The opioid epidemic was not much in the news back then, but perhaps she or others at the hospice were worried that my father would become addicted, or that we would somehow misuse a larger quantity of the painkiller.

That concern, according to well-established research,[7] is a big reason that end-of-life pain is often under-treated. It is a concern raised by patients, their caregivers, and even their physicians. But in end-of-life cases, the concern is misplaced. Research also shows that the addiction rate in the severely ill is remarkably low.[8]

When the US Centers for Disease Control and Prevention (CDC) issued new opiate-prescribing guidelines in March 2016, it exempted patients with active cancer, along with those under palliative care and end-of-life care. The CDC recognizes that the pain those patients experience is appropriately treated with opiates, with a low risk of addiction.[9]

After taking the morphine for a day, Dad complained that it wasn't helping. And, in retrospect, that isn't terribly surprising. When you take an oral dose of morphine, the liver metabolizes two-thirds of it. Only one-third reaches the bloodstream and actually delivers pain relief. On net, Dad was getting about 1 mg of morphine's pain killing power, an amount too low to make any difference for him.

While he was not getting pain relief, he was getting a disturbing side effect—severe constipation. All narcotic medications are notoriously constipating, as the warning labels clearly point out. But for some reason, the hospice failed to make sure my father also had the laxatives needed to cope with this entirely predictable and extremely uncomfortable condition.

Over the next hospice visits, Mom said that Dad stubbornly refused to rate his pain, while insisting that the morphine didn't help and that he had pain all over his body. But the hospice held firm: There would be no

7. Hunter Groninger and Jaya Vijayan. "Pharmacologic Management of Pain at the End of Life." *American Family Physician*, vol. 90, no. 1, pp. 26–32.

8. http://www.aafp.org/afp/2000/0201/p755.html.

9. http://www.cdc.gov/mmwr/volumes/65/rr/rr6501e1.htm.

change in the dose or frequency of the morphine. No other options for better pain treatment were offered. He was stuck with a low dose of pain medication that provided no relief.

Hospice care is based on the philosophy that "each of us has the right to die pain-free and with dignity."[10] But two weeks into Dad's second hospice enrollment, he continued to feel miserable. We found ourselves in the uncomfortable position of questioning the quality of his hospice care, and we were uncertain about what to do next.

Not long after that point, hospice nurse Barbara Cattermole appeared at Dad's bedside, setting off the chain of events that sent him, against his wishes, to the hospital, where the grim fate he'd planned so carefully to avoid now awaited him.

---

10. https://www.nhpco.org/about/hospice-care.

CHAPTER 4

Descent into Despair

Making someone die in a way that others approve, but he believes a horrifying contradiction of his life, is a devastating, odious form of tyranny.

—Ronald Dworkin, *Life's Dominion*

STARTING THAT THURSDAY, the treatment the hospital delivered to my father was guaranteed to include most everything he never wanted done to him. Rather than the palliative (comfort) care he wanted, he would be getting whatever it took to prolong his life. Treating him for a morphine overdose also meant that many other conditions—either long-standing or newly emerging ones—would also be treated. He still had a Do Not Resuscitate order, per Mom's instructions, which meant he would not get CPR or advanced resuscitation measures if his heart stopped beating. However, everything and anything else would now be done to prolong his life.

2:13 P.M., Thursday

Dad arrives in the ER of Schuylkill Medical Center. He is restless and moaning, but he is breathing normally, and his skin color is good. On the way there, in the ambulance with the paramedic, he was able to respond to her questions. Asked if he was having any pain, he'd said, "no." For the first time since entering hospice care, he is free from pain. The hospital asks Mom to give her consent to treat Dad, and Captain Durkin informs her that I will be in much worse trouble if Dad dies. Torn, she gives her consent.

3:40 P.M., Thursday

It is now well over four hours since Dad took the short-acting morphine. He is still breathing normally at 22 breaths a minute, but he is drowsier. The ER doctor orders a 2-milligram dose of Narcan to wake him up. It works almost immediately. Dad is livid at being in the hospital, his pain has roared back, and he knows I am in trouble. He pleads, "Don't hurt Barbara! Don't let them hurt Barbara!" Hospice workers, including Cattermole, appear, and he shouts, "Get the hell out of here!" He pulls out his IV and rips off the heart monitor. He refuses to allow the oxygen monitor to be placed on his finger. Mom tries desperately to calm him, but he remains angry and anguished.

7:00 P.M., Thursday

From the ER, Dad has been admitted to a telemetry unit. A nursing assistant has been assigned to observe him in his room at all times. Because a third party is present, I am finally permitted to see him. Assessing Dad's condition, a nurse has written, "He is lethargic but alert to stimuli." His bodily functions are being monitored by machines that beep and buzz, blinking in bright neon colors, continuously displaying his heart rate, blood pressure, respiratory rate, and the oxygen in his blood. Oxygen tubing loops around his chin and ears and then splits to enter each nostril. A transparent bag of IV fluid, hanging from a pole, slowly drips fluid into a vein in his arm. Gone is his favorite wool blanket; instead, he is encased in bright-white hospital linens. The plastic ID band on his wrist is a stark symbol that he now is in a place where the people caring for him do not know him. He is only a few miles from his home, but a world away from the comfort and familiarity of the only place where he had hoped to die.

8:05 P.M., Thursday

Dad's breathing rate drops to six breaths per minute. Dr. Hashin had ordered Narcan to be given if his breaths dropped below that rate, so it was close to the threshold of concern. For a second time a nurse gives Narcan, the morphine reversal drug, through his IV. As in the emergency room, he wakes up completely and the pain tears through him. He pulls off his gown, pulls off the heart monitor, and tries to climb out of the bed. For this behavior, he is rewarded by having his hands restrained so he cannot interfere with the treatment that will be inflicted on him. He remains restless and agitated for another hour, then becomes drowsy again.

Midnight, Thursday

Dad has spiked a fever, an early indication that some type of infection is brewing, most likely in the lungs or the urinary system. Any infection in a person who is already frail and dying would progress quite rapidly, as the person's immune system would be unable to mount an effective response.

Friday

Dad has become more lethargic; he no longer speaks, but when touched he opens his eyes and moans. Just a little more than twelve hours after being admitted to the hospital, Dad's skin begins to break down over the bony prominences on his buttocks and heels. His skin was completely intact before he was admitted to the hospital. But skin can break down quickly when a person is not turned frequently to relieve pressure on the bony areas of the body. Since there is a nursing assistant in his room at all times, I have no idea why Dad is not turned often enough to prevent these sores. Mom and Jim alternate visiting. They can't tell if Dad is even aware they are there. Throughout the day and into the night, Dad's skin burns hot with fever. He receives fever-reducing medicine and nurses place ice packs around his body to cool it down. For the second time, a urinary catheter is inserted to drain his bladder.

I am at home in Philadelphia, afraid to go to the hospital again to see him. I am terrified that anything I say will be misconstrued as evidence of some evil intent that would be used against me. I feel helpless and hopeless, overcome by a desolation more profound than I have ever experienced. I have failed my father.

Saturday

On Dad's third day in the hospital, his skin is still hot with fever. Mucus in his air passages causes a wheezing sound with each breath. Now he has pneumonia, and an antibiotic drips into his vein along with the IV fluid. His blood tests show his kidneys are failing. Mom sits with him, stroking his hand, speaking to him, but Dad doesn't respond.

Still home in Philadelphia, I am an emotional mess. I replay the disastrous events of the three previous days over and over in my mind, berating myself for ever mentioning morphine. Being arrested and rendered powerless to stop the violations of my father's wishes are a Kafkaesque nightmare. In numb disbelief, I can't eat or sleep. Our two teenage daughters helplessly watch as Joe and I weep and cling to each other. They silently withdraw from us and throw themselves into their schoolwork.

Early Sunday

It's Dad's fourth day in the hospital, and his kidney function dramatically worsens, raising the potassium level in his blood to a life-threatening range. The most effective way to treat this condition is with kidney dialysis. But since Dad is not on dialysis, the next-best treatment option is to give a medicine, Kayexalate, which lowers the potassium level—by causing massive diarrhea. So, this liquid medicine is put into his rectum, and it works as intended. Unfortunately, with the diarrhea, my father loses the top layer of his skin everywhere it touches—on his genitals, buttocks, and up to his sacrum on his lower back. His skin becomes open, raw, and red.

Reading a loved one's medical records is its own form of torture, particularly if you understand the terminology used and know what it means for the patient. You find out what your loved one endured, and it is nothing short of traumatizing. Mom gave me her daily report on Dad, but the explicit details in the medical record, especially about this skin loss on his most intimate and sensitive areas, broke my heart anew and will haunt me for as long as I live. A man who had weathered a childhood of adversity, survived one of the worst battles of World War II, achieved much through his own determination and tenacity, a man to whom it was vitally important to have his wishes respected, was helplessly submitting to painful, unwanted medical care that merely prolonged his death.

1:00 P.M., Sunday

Despite the aggressive medical treatment, Dad's major organs—heart, lung, and kidneys—are giving out. His ailing and weakened heart beats at twice the normal rate, as high as 140 beats per minute. At this point, Dad has multiple grave medical problems: pneumonia (which compromises his lung function and immune system), failing heart and kidneys, and uncontrolled blood sugars—all in a man almost ninety-four years old. He is obviously dying, but he is being made to live.

When Mom was asked to give her consent for Dad to be treated in the ER, she had no idea he would be subjected to so many painful interventions. She didn't know that the physician would feel compelled to correct any abnormal test result, and that attempts would be made to treat the end-stage medical diseases he had. She had been thrust into a decision-making role under tragic and confounding circumstances. Still, she had the presence of mind to insist that Barbara Cattermole from Hospice of Central Pennsylvania be banned from entering my father's room or having any connection to his case. To ensure that, the hospital nurses checked the identification badges of all hospice personnel who came to check on my father.

2:50 A.M., Monday

Dad's breathing becomes labored and his skin from his feet to his hips turns a mottled bluish color. He is completely unresponsive. A blood test shows that the pH, or acid level in his blood, is in the danger range. He has deteriorated into metabolic acidosis, a condition that will cause death if not reversed. Dad is placed on a bi-pap breathing machine; even though he is breathing on his own, the bi-pap will help balance carbon dioxide levels in his body. He is given several emergency medications to try to reverse the high acid level in his blood.

3:30 A.M., Monday

The phone jolts me awake. It is Mom, reporting that the hospital had called to say that Dad's condition had worsened and that she should come right away. I rush to get dressed and make the drive to Pottsville. The weather is as grim as my mood; freezing rain is blanketing the deserted black roadway of the Pennsylvania Turnpike. It's a dangerous drive, and I dread what I will find when I arrive.

5:00 A.M., Monday

In Pottsville, the freezing rain has left a sheet of ice for me on the steep path from the parking lot to the hospital entrance. Upstairs, on the sixth floor, I find that Mom, Jim, and Toni are already with Dad. He has a private room directly across from the nurses' station. The soft beige walls are accented with geometric patterns in muted shades—an improvement over the barren and antiseptic hospital rooms of the past.

When I look at Dad my heart sinks: a plastic mask that covers his nose and mouth is tightly strapped over his face, connecting him to the bi-pap respirator. His chest rises and falls as each gust of air pushes into his lungs. I had worked with these machines in the ER, and the discomfort from the tight fit they require is barely tolerable for patients who are awake. While it stops short of CPR, this sort of treatment is precisely what he had wanted to avoid, and what I and my family agreed would be a cruel imposition of futile treatment. This is Dad's fifth day in the hospital, and we all know it is time for this torture to end. We ask to speak with the attending physician, and the nursing supervisor requests we wait for Dr. Hashin to arrive for morning rounds, in about two hours.

I look at my father, lying motionless in the hospital bed, with IV and monitor tubing ascending from his arms and chest, and the rhythmic cycling of the bi-pap machine breaking the silence. A four-day stubble of white beard covers his cheeks and chin, and it strikes me how paradoxical it seems that even when the body is dying, parts of it, like hair, continue to grow. Both of his hands and forearms are so swollen from fluid—from his heart and kidney failure—that the skin covering them is taut and shiny, and they look like balloons that are ready to burst.

His bony legs appear as knobby sticks covered with a clean white sheet. Mom, exhausted but nervous, sits and stands, sits and stands, unable to find a place of comfort. Jim paces in and out of the room, and his wife stands by the doorway. I pull a chair up next to Dad's bed and hold his hand. What should have been a peaceful passing is now a bedside vigil with a sense of dread, my arrest looming over everything.

The bi-pap continues to force air into his lungs, and the IV keeps on dripping fluid into his veins. We know that none of these treatments will keep him alive or return him to health. We know that this is the day he will die. Seeing him lie there, suffering these interventions that totally violate his hopes, his dignity, his peace, and his legal directives is almost too much to bear.

I have not eaten anything since the previous evening, and I gratefully down a small can of ginger ale offered by the quiet and kindly nursing assistant. Hospital staff come in and out, and some of them avoid eye contact with me. Am I being harshly judged, or are they uncomfortable with the situation in which they have become unwilling participants? I do not blame the hospital staff in any way for what was done to my father. Once the hospice, then police, set events in motion, the health-care professionals at Schuylkill Medical Center were placed in the untenable position of prolonging the life of an elderly man against his expressed wishes, while the local police kept tabs on his condition. Much later, I learned from my attorney that the hospital staff were horrified to be a part of the terrible ordeal foisted upon my father.

Shortly after 8:00 A.M., Monday

Dr. Hashin arrives. A petite woman who approached us with warmth and empathy, she explains she has discontinued the antibiotic, as she feels it would only prolong Dad's death. Mom then asks her to honor Dad's wishes and end all life-prolonging treatment. Within minutes, the bi-pap machine is turned off, and only a slow IV drip and oxygen are left, although they, too, are later discontinued. A nurse comes in and injects a medicine into Dad's IV tubing. When I ask what she is giving him, she replies, without looking up, "Morphine." This is the first and only time in over four days he was given any medicine for his comfort. He would die with morphine in his system, but it was morphine administered by the hospital, not the allegedly suicidal dose I was falsely accused of handing him five days earlier. I stand next to Dad and gently rub his face where the mask edges have made red indentations in his skin. An open ulceration has already formed on the left side of his face from the pressure of the mask, and my eyes well with tears.

9:30 A.M., Monday

My sister Virginia arrives, followed by my nieces, and we all sit our deathbed vigils. Dad lies motionless and feverish, his heart pounding rapidly, with intermittent spasms of congested coughing. Yet he hangs on. With Mom looking exhausted and worn, I urge her to get a little rest, assuring her I will call immediately if things change. I settle in to stay by Dad's side until the very end.

Late morning, Monday

Virginia leaves after feeling unwell. Mom's pastor stops in, and we converse for a while. Pastor Schutt has been a great support to Mom through the family's whole nightmare, and to me, too, especially today. As Pastor and I sit talking next to Dad, Captain Durkin walks into the room and announces, "I understand your father is dying. I've called the coroner and he will be ordering an autopsy." This was a not-so-veiled hint that foul play was suspected. Durkin leaves after this brief announcement, but like a sinister presence who lurks in the shadows, he reappears right after Pastor Schutt leaves. While I sit next to Dad, holding his hand, Durkin scolds, "You're not supposed to be alone with your father. It's a condition of your bail." I am right next to the open door, in full view of the nurses' station, so his remark strikes me as callous and cruel. I want to punch him then and there. There is absolutely no reason for Durkin to intrude at my father's deathbed, unless he wants to remind me, and everyone involved with Dad's care, of the fate awaiting me in the so-called justice system.

2:00 P.M., Monday

Mom returns after a few hours of badly needed rest. We are all reassembled in Dad's room. We make small talk about the weather, catch up with the latest news of my nieces, then lapse into silence. It's too exhausting to force conversation, and we watch as Dad lies motionless in the bed except for occasional spasms of coughing.

4:30 P.M., Monday

The nurses ask us to step out of the room so they can change Dad and turn him. We walk down the hall to a waiting area, but a nurse immediately summons us to return. While being turned, Dad takes his last breath, and by the time we get back to his side, he is dead. I can only hope that somehow, on some level, he knew we were all there when it mattered.

We hold hands and cry, then go silent. I just feel numb. Staying with Dad, I go through the necessary motions like a zombie, first calling Joe, then some friends and relatives. My disabled sister, Linda, is on the way with her husband and daughter. Dad's death is going to be rough on her, as she had always been very close to my parents. When she arrives, thirty minutes too late, she is completely distraught. With her face turning red and tears streaming down her cheeks, she reaches out to Dad with her good arm from her wheelchair. My heart aches in her sorrow.

5:30 P.M., Monday

Schuylkill County Coroner David Moylan lumbers into the room. Without a trace of empathy, he matter-of-factly announces, "I'm the coroner, Dr. Moylan. We are conducting an investigation and you will have to leave the room while my assistant takes photographs and some blood samples." We silently file out of the room. It is clearly being treated as a crime scene, and I am the criminal, a crushing insinuation that compounds my grief and my agony at feeling that I failed my father. When the coroner finishes about twenty minutes later, we quietly return to the hospital room, touching Dad's hands and face, now cool and devoid of color. We tearfully say our final goodbyes, never to see Dad again.

I returned to work three days later but told no one of the events that happened or of my father's death. I wouldn't have known where to begin, and I had some hope that the case against me might not be pursued. Working in a hospital emergency room, I would keep exceptionally busy, so I could block out my personal turmoil. But as soon as I got home, my demons emerged, and I usually ended the day by sobbing my heart out. I just could not fathom why the police were so bent on pursuing this.

We had Dad's funeral on February 19, 2013, a miserable gray, frigid, and snowy day. Freezing rain had coated the snow with a layer of slick ice, and we could barely walk on the slippery paths. The service was in a tiny chapel located inside the gates of the cemetery—a beautiful arboretum of mature and varied trees surrounded by a stone wall, across the street from the house my parents lived in for decades. The chapel had no ramp, and four strong men struggled to lift Linda's wheelchair up the icy steps.

Tall stained-glass windows lined the chapel; their warm colors and the light that filtered through them proved a comforting contrast to the plain gray walls inside and the menacing skies outside. Mom had kept arrangements about the funeral quiet, and the wooden pews were half-filled with close family and friends. My father's ashes rested on a table next to his picture, in front of a single cross flanked by flowers on the altar. The gathering in the chapel enveloped us with compassion and support.

Pastor Schutt presided over the funeral in a Methodist service that my non-religious father agreed to well in advance, knowing it would comfort my mother. A military honor guard played "Taps" then crisply and expertly folded the American flag. A soldier handed it to Mom and solemnly said, "This flag is presented on behalf of a grateful nation and the United States Army as a token of appreciation for Joseph Yourshaw's honorable and faithful service in World War II." People seated behind me were sniffling, Mom dabbed her eyes with a handkerchief, and I felt a huge lump in my throat. A few people attending the funeral knew what had happened twelve days earlier; the others were completely unaware that his death was anything other than the predictable passing of an elderly man from this life. They knew nothing of the emotional anguish and medical torture inflicted on him in his final days.

I couldn't help thinking how the justice and medical systems are programmed to resist death at every turn, even for a ninety-three-year-old man who explicitly documented that he wanted no heroic end-of-life measures. With the legal charges against me, we were powerless to make the medical system respect my father's wishes when he was alive. But once he was dead, he was rightfully honored as a hero who served his country nobly in a time of war and who deserved the utmost respect.

After the funeral, Joe and I tried our best to resume a somewhat normal life by going through our daily routine, interrupted as it was with letters and calls from my attorney. But normalcy was denied us. Just seventeen days after Dad's death, Joe's father died. Remo Mancini, who had turned eighty-seven a month earlier, was leaving a medical appointment and literally dropped dead in a parking lot elevator. Passengers in the elevator immediately rendered what aid they could, but it was fruitless. Remo had terrible heart disease, so his death was not a shock. The timing, though, was awful. We were sorry that no family was with him when it happened, but mercifully, he had the kind of death that my own father hoped for—quick and painless. Exactly two weeks after my own father's funeral, we were again grieving, at my father-in-law's funeral.

Our sorrows were not yet done. Aunt Betty, my mom's only sibling, had been ailing for some time, and her condition dramatically worsened. She died on March 30, three weeks after my father-in-law's funeral. I began to wonder if we were cursed, and we all felt as if we were at the breaking point. The year 2013 had quickly become the worst year I had ever experienced, and my troubles were a long way from being over.

CHAPTER 5

The "Sanctity of Life"

The elected coroner system is just one cog in a very dysfunctional machine.

—Aviva Shen, writing in ThinkProgress

I WAS SURE the autopsy would confirm just how ill my father had been—terminally ill—and that I would be vindicated, but it would be a long wait for the results. Dad's body had been taken forty-four miles away, to Allentown, where it would be examined by Forensic Pathology Associates, the contractor hired by Schuylkill County. The autopsy findings would then be used to produce the official death certificate, issued by Schuylkill County Coroner David Moylan. My mother was anxious to get the death certificate, because she could not begin to settle dad's estate without it.

March passed without the autopsy results or the death certificate, and then April. The funeral director called the coroner's office weekly to check, but May turned into June, and still no death certificate.

Finally, on June 14, Mom received a call from the funeral director that the death certificate was ready. She and my brother drove to the coroner's office to pick it up. That evening, I was working a shift in the emergency room. My husband made an urgent call to me at work—something he rarely did. He said, "Do you have moment? Mom just called about Dad's death certificate. You better sit down." In an ominous tone, he continued, "Here's what it said . . . 'cause of death: morphine toxicity complicating hypertensive atherosclerotic cardiovascular disease; manner of death: homicide.'"

"Homicide!" I felt like I'd just taken a shotgun blast to my chest. I knew very well my father did not die from a morphine overdose. An overdose of this short-acting form of morphine kills within minutes or hours—you simply stop breathing. It does not take days. My father was breathing normally for many hours after he took the morphine. In fact, when he first received the reversal agent, Narcan, in the emergency room—four hours after he took the morphine—he was drowsy but still breathing normally at twenty-two breaths per minute. My father never stopped breathing until he died, *five days* after taking the morphine dose that supposedly killed him.

The coroner's incomprehensible ruling on my father's death left me searching for an explanation. And the evidence was not hard to find. While we were waiting for the autopsy and death certificate, Coroner Moylan had been busy in the world of politics.

In Pennsylvania, the county coroner is an elected position. It is a curiously antiquated way to fill a highly specialized job that carries such heavy responsibilities. A coroner's job is to investigate deaths that are unexplained or unnatural, and determine, if possible, the cause and manner of death. The findings are used to bring criminal cases and identify potentially significant threats to public health.

A candidate for coroner in Pennsylvania does not have to be a physician or even have any medical training. He or she need only be a United States citizen, a resident of the county for at least a year, and age eighteen or older.[1] Once elected, Pennsylvania county coroners must attend a four-day basic education course where they learn about crime-scene investigation, toxicology, forensic autopsies, and legal duties of a coroner.[2] Each year in office, they must attend eight hours of continuing education.[3]

1. http://www.legis.state.pa.us/WU01/LI/LI/US/HTM/1955/0/0130..HTM, Article IV, section 413.
2. http://www.pacode.com/secure/data/037/chapter199/s199.21.html.
3. http://www.pacode.com/secure/data/037/chapter199/s199.41.html.

David Moylan happened to be more qualified than most for the position of coroner—he is a licensed physician. (His immediate predecessor was a retired state police corporal, and the coroner elected before that was a funeral director.) However, Moylan is not a pathologist nor a medical examiner, which is a physician trained to do autopsies and forensic death examinations. Moylan is a radiation oncologist, delivering treatment to cancer patients. He also had other interests that would come to light as my case proceeded.

While my father's death certificate was in limbo, Moylan was busy keeping his name in the local Pottsville newspaper, the *Republican Herald*. In April, he had hosted a presentation by the Pennsylvania Pro-Life Federation at his cancer treatment center.[4] The group focuses most of its energies on opposing abortion, but it also stridently opposes medical aid-in-dying.[5]

After releasing my father's death certificate in June, Moylan continued to groom his public image by holding a forum on suicide prevention at his place of business on July 18.[6] It was the prelude to his big announcement, which occurred three days later: Moylan hosted a "Celebration of Life Picnic" and declared his candidacy for Congress, seeking the Republican nomination for the 17th District in the 2014 election.[7]

Three weeks later, congressional candidate Moylan appeared on the *Sam LeSante Show*, a right-leaning television talk show in northeastern Pennsylvania. "When I ran for coroner, I ran as a pro-life coroner," he said. "And you might say what the heck is a pro-life coroner? But it's very important that every decision you make as coroner to determine the cause and manner of death—see how does it affect the sanctity of life? So, I've done that for the last year and a half."[8]

When asked in a later interview why he chose to run for Congress, Moylan declared, "It just boiled down to one primary issue . . . the sanctity of human life. It's so important to defend human life, from

4. http://republicanherald.com/news/pro-life-group-spreads-message-at-simon-kramer-cancer-institute-1.1470023.
5. http://www.paprolife.org/fact-sheets.
6. http://republicanherald.com/news/public-forum-suicide-is-the-most-preventable-death-1.1522927.
7. http://republicanherald.com/news/county-coroner-moylan-announces-bid-for-congress-1.1524061.
8. Remarks, *The Sam LeSante Show*, 8/7/2013, https://www.youtube.com/watch?v=bmhakP43hRk.

conception to natural death."[9] And in a candidates' forum, he promised that the first legislation he would introduce in Congress would be a "Human Life Amendment" to the US Constitution.[10] However, his concern for the "sanctity of life" didn't stop him from driving drunk in April 1995, before he was elected coroner—an inconvenient aspect of his record he had to admit in his congressional campaign.

When my brother, Jim, picked up the death certificate, he'd asked Moylan why he'd concluded that my father's death was a homicide. Moylan answered, "Because this was an assisted suicide, so that makes it a homicide." Moylan had seized on my case as a way to show off his commitment to uphold "the sanctity of life" all the way to "natural death."

I would not be the only one to conclude that Moylan's damning claim about my father's death—"homicide"—was politically motivated. His agenda was clear: He was openly courting a conservative religious constituency to advance his political ambitions. Later, as I dug into the records made available through the criminal case against me, I'd discover many ways the investigation into my father's death raised questions about Moylan's professional conduct and how he produced his politically biased conclusion.

Some of the most popular television dramas in America are shows like *CSI: Crime Scene Investigation*, which depict modern crime investigators as highly skilled scientists using state-of-the-art laboratory and computer equipment, gathering and processing evidence in careful and meticulous ways as they work to bring perpetrators of crime to justice. This makes for good story lines and suspenseful viewing, but, like many things dramatized in Hollywood, it is far from reality.

There is a huge variation in how states and local governments across the United States handle death investigations. Many states, like Pennsylvania, entrust the work to the county coroner. Nationwide, 82%

9. https://www.youtube.com/watch?v=pAMjnO5kmeA&feature=youtube_gdata.

10. http://www.pahomepage.com/story/d/story/meet-the-candidates-17th-congressional-district/17900/2zKbbvLzkWg_MxTrvFcEQ.

of county coroners are elected[11] and they need not have any specialized training in forensics or pathology. In some states and localities, death investigations are handled by a medical examiner, physicians who may or may not be pathologists with experience or training relevant to the highly specialized job. (The large urban areas in Pennsylvania use medical examiners.)

The result: In some jurisdictions, death investigations are highly professional and performed under strict protocols. In others, the work is more haphazard and open to error and bias.

"A lot of people see TV and *CSI* and they think that's how it really is. But really, it varies from excellent to *absolutely lousy*," said Vincent DiMaio, MD, former chief medical examiner of San Antonio, Texas, in a 2011 Frontline production: *Post Mortem: Death Investigation in America.* "I'm saying that in this country, many medico-legal offices are producing garbage."[12]

In my father's case, the autopsy report was filled with obvious errors. The pathologist who performed the autopsy, Dr. Rameen Starling-Roney, wrote in his report,

> *According to information provided by the Schuylkill County Coroner's Office, the decedent was a 92-year-old white male who was at hospice care when he asked his daughter (who is a nurse) to give him morphine so he would die. She gave him the remainder of the bottle. He went into a coma, his nurse came in and the daughter told exactly what happened. The nurse called police and the daughter subsequently told them what happened. The daughter was arrested. The father was taken to the hospital and given Narcan; he woke up and reportedly was angry, asking for his daughter. He lived for the next three days in the hospital; his hospital course was significant for worsening respiratory distress. He has no known history of terminal cancer. His medical history includes uncontrolled diabetes; he stopped taking his medications in 2011. He reportedly*

11. https://www.ncjrs.gov/pdffiles1/nij/grants/228091.pdf, p. 247.
12. http://www.pbs.org/wgbh/pages/frontline/post-mortem/, minute 5:17–5:47.

had suicidal ideations and would not listen to nurses while in hospice care.[13]

My father was not ninety-two years old; he was ninety-three, just six weeks shy of ninety-four. He was not living at a hospice; he lived at home and received home-based hospice care. After taking the morphine, Dad did not go into a coma, which is a state of deep unconsciousness for a prolonged or indefinite period. The responding paramedic's written report indicated that Dad was "alert to verbal stimuli" and that he answered her questions.[14] Hospice nurse Barbara Cattermole documented that my father "responds to voice, able to focus with eyes."[15] Dad died on the fifth day of his hospitalization, not the third day. He quickly developed a fever and pneumonia in the hospital. Contrary to the autopsy's claim, he didn't develop true respiratory distress until the last day, when the pneumonia developed into overwhelming sepsis, as the infection spread from his lungs throughout his body. As for reported suicidal ideations, there were no such reports; in fact, the hospice records specifically noted that my father denied having suicidal thoughts. The pathologist wrote in his autopsy report, "the body is that of a well-developed, well-nourished white male." In fact, my father had significant weight loss. For weeks, he had barely eaten anything besides candy and soda, and his clothing was so loose that it sagged on his bony frame.

Early in preparing my defense against the criminal charges, my attorney took the autopsy report to an experienced and qualified pathologist. After reading it, the pathologist threw it down on his desk and declared, "This is nonsense!"

Later in my research, I asked a highly respected, experienced forensic toxicologist, Dr. James Roberts, vice chair of the Department of Emergency Medicine of Drexel University College of Medicine in Philadelphia, to review my father's medical records and autopsy report. His bottom-line conclusion: "This was not a lethal level of morphine,

13. Forensic Pathology Associates Autopsy Report Joseph Yourshaw.
14. Patient Care Report, Pottsville-Schuylkill Haven Area EMS.
15. 2013 Hospice of Central Pennsylvania Record of Joseph Yourshaw, p. 75.

by any means." Because my father was drowsy but not unconscious, Dr. Roberts concluded that the large amount of morphine he'd consumed was likely therapeutic—the correct dose to relieve his pain, and not a fatal dose. He affirmed that Dad had developed metabolic acidosis and felt it was likely he died from pneumonia.

Dr. Roberts flagged several major issues with how the evidence in my father's death was gathered and analyzed. Most astonishing, the coroner issued the death certificate *before* the lab produced the results from testing the blood drawn from Dad right after he died. The lab report on that post-mortem blood sample was issued on June 18, 2013—four days *after* coroner Moylan issued the death certificate. Moylan reached his shocking and erroneous conclusion—that Dad died of "morphine toxicity"—without the lab's report on how much morphine was in his bloodstream when he died.

The delay in testing was not the lab's fault—Moylan's office had held onto the sample for three-and-a-half months before sending it to be analyzed. Even if Moylan had the lab report showing how much morphine Dad had in his blood when he died, a critical question would have remained unanswered. The hospital had given him a dose of morphine during his last hours of life. How much of the morphine left in his system came from that hospital dose and how much came from the supposedly suicidal dose he gave himself five days earlier? A simple post-mortem blood test, showing total morphine levels, does not answer that question.

When the post-mortem blood test was finally performed, it produced a bizarre result: The morphine level in my father's blood was exactly the same as it had been five days before he died. "It's totally unfathomable that these levels were identical," Dr. Roberts told me, because morphine levels will fall over time as the body metabolizes the compound. "It leads me to believe the lab may have tested the same samples twice," he said.

Finally, Dr. Roberts noted that the reliability of both sets of blood tests was called into question, because the samples were collected in the wrong kind of specimen tube. Normal forensic lab protocols call for toxicology samples to be collected in gray-top tubes, which contain sodium fluoride as a preservative.[16] Indeed, the forensic laboratory that processed my father's blood says on its website that blood for toxicology analysis *must* be submitted in gray-top tubes.[17]

However, my father's blood samples were sent to the lab in specimen tubes with green tops. These tubes contain the additive heparin, which Dr. Roberts said does not stop metabolism and does not stop the specimen from degrading. In these green-top tubes, the red or white blood cells can continue to remain active, which affects the quality of the blood sample and can alter the toxicological results.

"It is anyone's guess what effect heparin would have on the drug level in the sample" taken from Dad, Dr. Roberts told me. His opinion cast grave doubt onto the lab results that supposedly show my father died of morphine toxicity.

The worst of the inaccuracies in the autopsy report is the claim that my father "asked his daughter (who is a nurse) to give him morphine so he would die." I never said that. Neither the hospice nurse, the police captain, nor the coroner heard me say that—or heard what my father said to me.

The autopsy's claim on this point is fourth-hand hearsay—misinformation handed along the chain of authority, as in the children's game of telephone. The hospice nurse either misheard my explanation of what my father said, or simply jumped to her own shocking conclusion about what happened. She relayed her false account of our conversation to the police captain, who passed it on to the coroner.

From there, it's easy to see how this damning claim would have ended up in the autopsy report. Dr. Starling-Roney's write-up indicates that both Captain Durkin and Coroner Moylan were present at the autopsy.

It's highly unusual for a key witness in the case—the police captain—to be present at the autopsy, which is a supposedly independent

16. http://medind.nic.in/jal/t08/i2/jalt08i2p96.pdf.
17. http://www.nmslabs.com/uploads/PDF/Postmortem%20Submission%20Process%20Sheet.pdf.

fact-finding process. (Coroners are not routinely present at autopsies, although they may attend to enhance their learning.)

The presence of two other investigators with a strong attachment to a preexisting theory of the case could have easily influenced the pathologist's error-filled report on my father's death. As the National Academy of Sciences noted in a 2009 report that called for widespread reforms to improve the investigation of crimes, forensic analyses may be "influenced by knowledge regarding the background of the suspect and the investigator's theory of the case."[18] The National Academy of Forensic Examiners strongly encourages forensic pathologists to maintain their independence from law enforcement, and feels they should be protected from political pressure or intimidation in determining the cause of death.[19] Investigative journalist Radley Balko and Mississippi Innocence Project Director Tucker Carrington write that interactions with law enforcement can bias the forensic pathologist's conclusions: "In fact, studies have shown that the more details crime lab analysts know about a case before conducting their analysis, the more likely they are to come up with false positives."[20]

To Dr. Roberts, the forensic toxicology expert who reviewed my father's autopsy report, the flawed investigation and erroneous conclusion were not a surprise. He told me that about one in every four death rulings by coroners is wrong. That is a shocking error rate, but it's not surprising, considering that most coroners may run for office with no professional qualifications whatsoever and receive minimal training once elected.

The rampant flaws in this country's forensic investigations were extensively documented in the 2009 report by the National Academy of Sciences (NAS).[21] Flawed testing and analysis often receive unwarranted

18. http://ag.ca.gov/meetings/tf/pdf/2009_NAS_report.pdf, recommendation 5, S-18.

19. https://netforum.avectra.com/public/temp/ClientImages/NAME/00df032d-ccab-48f8-9415-5c27f173cda6.pdf.

20. Radley Balko and Tucker Carrington. *The Cadaver King and the Country Dentist.* New York: PublicAffairs, 2018, p. 174.

21. http://ag.ca.gov/meetings/tf/pdf/2009_NAS_report.pdf.

credibility in court, the report found. Part of the problem, the report noted, is that inexact and misrepresentative expert testimony can lead judges to admit faulty evidence in a case.[22]

The report made many recommendations for improvement, but one of those recommendations was not new. The call to abolish the coroner system in the United States was first issued in 1928, by the very same research body, the National Academy of Sciences, and the recommendation has been repeated several times since then.

The 1928 report characterized the coroner's office as an "anachronistic institution predating the Magna Carta," and said it "has conclusively demonstrated its incapacity to perform the functions customarily required of it."[23] The coroner's office should be replaced by a medical examiner's office, the report said, "headed by a scientifically trained and competent pathologist, selected and retained under civil service, and compensated by a salary that will attract people of genuine scientific training and ability."[24]

Attempts have been made to improve things. In 1998, the National Institute for Justice developed guidelines for death scene investigations. When the guidelines were field-tested on a hundred coroners and deputy coroners in Indiana, though, the results were dismal—almost 80% failed the test. The tests were repeated in other states, and the failure rates were similar. Even coroners with medical backgrounds (except forensic pathologists) had similar failure rates as non-medical coroners.[25]

Despite the political bias and systematic flaws in how my father's death was investigated, the verdict the coroner rendered—that Dad died due to morphine toxicity—would be used against me. When my case made it to court, critical questions would revolve around how, when, and why my father received morphine.

---

22. http://ag.ca.gov/meetings/tf/pdf/2009_NAS_report.pdfS-3.
23. https://www.nap.edu/read/12589/chapter/11#242.
24. http://ag.ca.gov/meetings/tf/pdf/2009_NAS_report.pdf, p. 9-1.
25. https://www.nap.edu/read/10792/chapter/6#20-21.

CHAPTER 6

"Action is the antidote to despair."

Not everything that is faced can be changed. But nothing can be changed until it is faced.

—James Baldwin

I WAS NOW an accused felon facing up to ten years in prison for trying to help my long-suffering father reduce his pain. I was sure the charges were based on a horrible misunderstanding that my attorney could easily clarify and get resolved. Dying patients have the constitutional right to pain relief, and my father was exercising that right. The Pottsville police never should have interfered with that.

But as noted historian Howard Zinn has pointed out, "The fact that you have a constitutional right doesn't mean you're going to get that right. Who has the power on the spot? The policemen on the street."[1]

Once police ignored my father's constitutional right and arrested me, there was some hope the prosecutor's office might not pursue the case. After an arrest, prosecutors may decide they cannot prove the case beyond a reasonable doubt. They may have other, higher priorities for their limited resources. Or they may exercise discretion and decide the interests of justice would be served by dropping the charges. I've since been told by prosecutors elsewhere in the country that they would never pursue a case like mine.

1. Howard Zinn. *Failure to Quit: Reflections of an Optimistic Historian.* South End, 2002, p.84.

But I got no help on that score from the Schuylkill County district attorney. She decided to bow out of the case and refer it to the state attorney general's office. Hearing that news, I was shocked. No longer was this a relatively minor local case that could be resolved by those closest to the events. It was starting to look like I was in grave trouble.

The county district attorney, Karen Byrnes-Noon, had what might seem like a plausible explanation for taking herself off the case: She has been a friend of my sister Linda since high school. According to the American Bar Association's Criminal Justice Standards, a prosecutor's professional judgment should not be affected by "personal interests or relationships."[2] She could argue that handing things over to the state attorney general would bring a properly independent perspective to the case.

However, given Schuylkill County's sparse population, almost anyone charged in criminal cases there will know someone who works in the local criminal justice system. If friendship with a defendant's family member is a valid reason to avoid handling a case, then local district attorneys in Pennsylvania's forty-eight lightly populated rural counties[3] are going to send a lot of work to the state attorney general's office.

I suspect Byrnes-Noon had another reason for ducking out. She had been in office only a year, having been appointed to fill a vacancy. A mere three weeks before my arrest, she had announced she would run for election to a full four-year term. My case was likely to stir controversy she didn't need. Either decision she made—drop the charges or pursue them—could jeopardize her chances of winning the election. It was safer to punt.

I had been hoping my attorney would tell me, "I will explain everything, and the charge will almost certainly be dropped." Instead, my husband and I handed over a $10,000 retainer and girded ourselves for a longer fight—one that would ultimately cost ten times that much.

---

2. http://www.americanbar.org/groups/criminal_justice/standards/ProsecutionFunctionFourthEdition.html.
3. http://www.rural.palegislature.us/demographics_about_rural_pa.html.

The Pennsylvania state attorney general at the time was Kathleen Kane, the first female and first Democrat ever elected to the office. At first, I was hopeful. Though a Catholic, she had campaigned as pro-choice on abortion. That stance suggested she supported a person's right to self-determination in deeply personal health-care decisions, rather than following the dictates of a particular religious doctrine.

If that were true, it didn't affect the decision her office made in my case. We soon learned that the attorney general would proceed with the charges against me.

The case was assigned to a career prosecutor, Senior Deputy Attorney General Anthony Forray. I still had hope that he or his superiors would realize the truth of what happened and agree that pursuing the case was a miscarriage of justice.

But my attorney reported that Forray made a shocking accusation. Forray said he'd talked to the hospice and learned that I had called them to ask for morphine. Then he asserted, "I think she forced the morphine down her father's throat."

When my attorney relayed the news, I exploded.

"That is absolute bullshit! Sure, I called for the morphine because he needed it. He had nothing for pain! A hospice is supposed to provide pain relief for people who are dying. Hell, my dad received morphine during his first hospice enrollment, no questions asked! He asked for his medicine, I handed it to him, and he took it."

Forray's incendiary accusation told me that I was in for a nasty fight. I could not helplessly sit back and allow my fate to be determined by this inflammatory falsehood.

I was ready to dig into hospice and hospital records and show exactly what happened. But my attorney informed me that in Pennsylvania, the defense has no right to "discovery"—obtaining evidence in the case by subpoena if necessary—until after the preliminary hearing. I could not get the records I needed until then.

In the meantime, I wasn't going to just sit around and mope about my fate. A quote from Joan Baez helped me find the psychological strength I needed to carry on: "Action is the antidote to despair." I wrote it out in bold marker, pinned it on the front of the refrigerator, and it became my mantra. I would do whatever I could to fight this unjust charge, and if the AG was hell-bent on bringing me down, I would not go quietly.

Spending hour after hour, day after day on internet research, books, and journals, I found that it is common for the local community to strongly support defendants who were being prosecuted for "assisting a suicide."

In one case from Missouri, a young man was being prosecuted after he and a despondent friend had made a suicide pact and purchased a gun together. The friend shot himself and died, but upon seeing the bloody consequences, the young man changed his mind and fled the scene. Put on trial for voluntary manslaughter, he was acquitted by a jury.[4] I figured that any attorney who could win that case was worth talking to, and she temporarily joined my defense team as an adviser.

I also found many other cases besides mine where police lie about what happened in a case.[5] It was this research that brought to my attention the term "testilying." And it wasn't difficult to find cases where prosecutors seemed to care more about playing to the voters who elect them rather than pursuing a just outcome—especially prosecutors with ambitions to run for higher office. It was sobering to know that the same forces I was confronting were so pervasive and so powerful in the American criminal justice system.

One of the most important steps I took resulted from a simple suggestion offered by a friend. "You should get in touch with a group called Compassion and Choices," the friend said. "They support people facing end-of-life decisions. They might be able to help." Compassion and Choices would offer valuable advice on legal questions and media strategy, allowing our side to take the initiative in fighting back.

When my attorneys finally had a chance to meet with Prosecutor Forray, they came away encouraged. The meeting was amicable, and they felt there was a good chance the charge against me would be resolved.

4. http://www.stltoday.com/news/local/crime-and-courts/jury-acquits-man-in-rare-assisted-suicide-case/article_5cfda5dc-c648-59b0-bdda-f0e5a4ed1eb0.html.

5. http://www.nytimes.com/2013/02/03/opinion/sunday/why-police-officers-lie-under-oath.html.

But it wasn't long before our hopes were dashed. Just two days later, the prosecutor sent my attorney an email making a bare-knuckles threat: waive my rights to a preliminary hearing, or I'd have absolutely no hope of ever getting any kind of plea deal.

"I am not going to offer a misdemeanor or other resolution without hearing something that changes my current view of the case," Forray wrote. "I have suggested you should waive the Preliminary Hearing, you will get everything in discovery."

"If you want a Preliminary Hearing you have that right. [But] put this on the front page of the paper and try to aggressively attack the hospice witnesses, the EMT or the police at a Preliminary Hearing and I guarantee you have a zero chance of a plea resolution." Noting that the charge is a second-degree felony, Forray wrote, "the standard range for conviction is jail time. She has a lot to lose, beyond her nursing license."

Oh, and by the way, don't bother trying to change his mind. "I am done talking about this case," he wrote.[6]

In other words: Take my threat lying down, or take your chances.

In the American justice system, the prosecutor has near-absolute power in negotiating plea bargains. Unlike me, most defendants don't have the financial resources needed to wage a fair fight in court against the prosecution. Their lawyers are likely to be public defenders—dedicated and experienced trial attorneys who carry enormous caseloads and have limited funding for hiring investigators or expert witnesses. If unable to make bail, defendants may be stuck in jail for months, even years, as their cases drag out. They are already being punished, simply for being poor.

It's no wonder the threat of a long jail sentence is often all that is needed for defendants to waive their rights and accept a plea bargain, even if they are innocent. Plea bargaining is the major reason why prosecutors can claim they have conviction rates of 90 to 95%.

At this stage, I was facing the full investigative and prosecutorial power of the state, without access to the evidence I was sure would prove

6. Email from Pennsylvania Senior Deputy Attorney General Anthony Forray to my attorney, dated June 6, 2013.

my innocence. From what they could see, my attorneys didn't like the odds and recommended pursuing a plea deal.

But there was no way I was going to plead guilty to this trumped-up charge. I kept thinking, "This is an outrage! I can't allow them to intimidate me!"

I felt I was being railroaded on the flimsiest allegations, and I was losing confidence in my legal representation. My lawyers were doing what they thought was best, given their limited understanding of the facts and evidence in the case. I don't fault them for that, so I am not naming them. But Forray was clearly being a hardline prosecutor, using all his fearsome power to intimidate me into capitulating. I needed someone just as hard-nosed to represent me.

I refused to waive my preliminary hearing and started looking for a lawyer who was just as eager to fight back as I was.

At the time, the Pottsville newspaper was covering a supposed scandal involving the supervisor of the local sewer authority, David Kraft. The Pennsylvania attorney general's office had charged him with two felonies for allegedly adding too much chlorine to treated wastewater that flows into the Schuylkill River and then falsifying his reports to cover up the excess discharges.

The key to Kraft's "crime," according to the prosecution, was his failure to average the amounts of chlorine the plant put into the discharged water. Doing so meant that he under-reported the amount of chlorine sent into the Schuylkill River.[7]

There was only one problem with that claim: At trial, the prosecution's main witness, the state inspector in charge of monitoring the plant, admitted he had never told Kraft that the daily chlorine discharges had to be averaged. When Kraft filed the reports in question, it was an innocent error, not a criminal act. And if it was such a horrible crime, it was odd that earlier state inspections failed to uncover it. The state inspector

7. http://republicanherald.com/news/sewer-authority-s-plant-operator-goes-on-trial-1.1499653.

admitted that three years of inspections by the watchdog agency had found nothing wrong at the sewer authority.

Kraft's attorney told the jury, "This case represents the worst of our government, an abuse of power, a bureaucracy unchecked. The bullying stops here. This man is innocent."[8] The jury deliberated less than thirty minutes and acquitted Kraft.

The attorney who picked apart the attorney general's bogus case was Pottsville native Fred Fanelli.

I'd found the fighting lawyer I needed.

Fred Fanelli's office is located off the main commercial street in Pottsville, in a building that once was the Necho Allen Hotel, an opulent landmark during Pottsville's heyday as a coal town with a small but wealthy upper class.

Fanelli's firm occupies the first floor, which is beautifully appointed with spacious marble stairs and walls. One can imagine the scene at the turn of the twentieth century, when anthracite coal mining was at its zenith, as the Pottsville elite arrived here for formal social affairs, bedecked in their finest garments. The coal barons were able to enjoy an ostentatious lifestyle while the miners and children who worked slavishly to dig out the coal lived in poverty and died young or were disabled from the dangerous conditions in the mines.

For the former Necho Allen Hotel, its current use was certainly an ironic twist of fate: Once a bastion of privilege, it was now occupied by someone who'd dedicated his life to upholding the principles of justice by defending people accused of wrongdoing.

When I explained what happened, and why I was innocent, Fanelli agreed to represent me. Mine was the kind of case that reaffirmed his passion for criminal defense work, a passion based on personal experience.

"When I was in high school," he told me, "I wrote a paper for English class about the American West. I was fascinated by the history of how the

8. http://republicanherald.com/news/sewer-authority-s-plant-operator-goes-on-trial-1.1499653.

country expanded across the continent, and I'd read all kinds of books about it. It was a damn good paper.

"But my teacher decided that no high school student could write a paper that good. She was convinced that I'd plagiarized it. I was outraged. You do all this great work, you're really proud of it, and then you get accused of cheating. I had to come in with all my books and notes I'd made for the paper to prove that it was my own work."

The incident was resolved in Fanelli's favor, but he said, "I never forgot what it felt like to be wrongly accused."

Though Fanelli thought he could win my case, he recognized that, at this stage of the process, it was not a fair fight. The state held all the cards; until the preliminary hearing was over, I'd have no access to the medical and hospice records that would show how wrong the state's charges were. At the preliminary hearing, Fanelli would not be presenting a defense; he would only question the witnesses and evidence presented by the prosecution. The same legally unsophisticated, restaurant-owner-turned-magistrate-judge would preside.

Making matters worse, the magistrate revealed that he'd been tainted by information fed to him outside of a proper court setting. When Fanelli called to ask for a continuance, magistrate judge Reilly asked, "Has the charge been amended to homicide because she forced the morphine down his throat?"

That was the same outrageous claim that prosecutor Forray had made to my first attorney. It's one thing for a lawyer to make such an inflammatory and unsupported accusation in a conversation outside of court. It's another altogether for a supposedly impartial judge to repeat the accusation before he has formally heard any properly offered testimony or seen admissible evidence to support it. I could only conclude that magistrate Reilly had had an *ex parte* communication (a forbidden private communication between a judge and a participant in a legal case) about my case—a gross violation of judicial ethics standards.[9]

9. http://www.americanbar.org/groups/professional_responsibility/publications/model_code_of_judicial_conduct/model_code_of_judicial_conduct_canon_2/rule2_9expartecommunications.html.

At this point, we had only one way to seize the initiative. Ironically, it was a tactic that prosecutor Forray himself hinted at. Compassion and Choices and Fanelli both recommended going to the media with my side of the case.

They believed the public would sympathize with me and criticize the attorney general for pursuing charges, but I was hesitant. I valued my privacy, so much so that I never even had a social media presence on Facebook, Twitter, or Instagram. I was just a regular, hard-working person who lived in relative obscurity, which was fine by me. Going public would put the rest of my family under intense media scrutiny too. How would it affect my husband and children? What about Mom?

It was also a high-stakes gamble. I'd likely lose my career—a hospital can't employ a nurse who's accused of trying to help someone kill himself. And there was no guarantee that the media coverage would help. It could even backfire. If the prosecutor became so outraged that we had gone to the media, he might decide to pile on more charges to ratchet up the pressure on me.

On the other hand, I didn't have any better options. Once a court hearing was held, the case would be public knowledge—the local Pottsville newspaper regularly reported on criminal cases—so I'd have to quit my job anyway. The question was not if the media would know about my case, but when and how.

Fanelli warned me that the prosecution, after vilifying me in court, would typically walk out and hand the media a prepared statement, making its one-sided case against me. Its "spin" on the case would be the first to take hold in the public's mind. The prosecution might even feed the media the lie that I forced morphine into my father to assist his death. If that totally fabricated version of events got out first, it would be hard for us to erase it with the truth.

It was significant that the police and the prosecution had kept quiet about the case, instead of boasting to the media, which is routine when they think it will bring favorable publicity. Perhaps they knew that prosecuting a loving daughter who had simply handed her dying father the pain medicine he'd requested would not go over well with the public.

For now, it seemed that I could either do nothing and just wait for the preliminary hearing or decide to fight. I chose to fight.

We would try to do what prosecutor Forray had specifically warned us not to do: "Put it on the front page of the paper."

Before going public, I had to have the meeting at work that I'd long been dreading. I went to my manager's office, and she greeted me with a smile. She saw the pained expression on my face and asked if everything was OK. "No," I whispered, then broke down into tears.

"What's wrong?" she asked.

"I have no idea where to begin." I struggled to explain the details coherently. The words tumbled out—arrested, wrongly accused, handed my father morphine, hospice nurse believed my dad was trying to kill himself, my father's grim death in the hospital, the felony charge of attempted suicide.

My manager came from behind her desk, put her arm around me, and allowed me to cry onto her shoulder. "I don't believe their accusations," she declared. "As far as I'm concerned you can continue to work as long as you want. And you have my support throughout this terrible ordeal."

However, I knew she would not be the ultimate decision-maker; she had to report this to the hospital administration. Sure enough, I received a call from her fifteen minutes later, regretfully telling me I had to go on an unpaid leave of absence.

Just two days before the preliminary hearing, our gamble paid off. On July 30, 2013, news of my case broke on the front page of the local section in the *Philadelphia Inquirer*: "Phila. woman charged with aiding death."

It was a sympathetic account. Kathryn Tucker, the director of legal advocacy with Compassion and Choices, was quoted saying my father "had a right to relieve his suffering. The Supreme Court has ruled in a pair of cases that I brought in the mid-1990s that dying patients have a right to all the pain medication they need, even if it advances the time of death."

Reporter Marie McCullough noted the questionable conclusions on the death certificate and pointed out that Captain Durkin and Coroner Moylan attended the autopsy. She also mentioned Coroner Moylan's recent decision to run for US Congress on a pro-life platform.

The article subtly summed up the absurdity of the case by ending with another quote from Tucker: "It is very hard to see what would motivate a prosecutor to charge a daughter at the bedside of her dying father with a crime when she does nothing more than hand him his medication."

The *Inquirer* story quickly vaulted me from obscurity to major news. It went out on the Associated Press newswire, followed by coverage on Philadelphia and Scranton TV news stations, and even National Public Radio. Fanelli, quoted by another journalist, made the key point that "It's nonsense to assert that one can die from morphine toxicity from a dose taken five days earlier."

All the publicity meant there would be a huge media turnout at my preliminary hearing, likely producing more bad coverage for the prosecution.

Stung by all the unfavorable media attention, prosecutor Forray was outraged. We had done exactly what his email warned us not to do. He served notice that he would file an emergency request with a higher court, asking it to impose a gag order on all parties in the case. That hearing would be held right before my preliminary hearing, at nine A.M. on August 1.

Would I be allowed to continue talking about my case? Could my attorneys mount a strong enough attack on the prosecution's case to get the charges thrown out of court?

In two days, we would find out.

CHAPTER 7

Hearsay, Speculation, and Guess

A hundred suspicions don't make a proof.
— Fyodor Dostoyevsky, *Crime and Punishment*

THE SCHUYLKILL COUNTY Courthouse is a sturdy, broad-shouldered, Romanesque revival building built in the prosperous coal mining times of the late nineteenth century. Five stories high, it has a tastefully embellished brown sandstone exterior with a clock tower 170 feet high. More recent additions and renovations have not compromised the original building's grandeur.

Inside, Court of Common Pleas President Judge William Baldwin would decide whether a gag order was warranted in my case. His courtroom fit the classic image you see on TV shows—wood paneling, the judge's desk up high, a jury box off to the side, tables for the defense and prosecution, seating in the back for spectators.

Waiting for Judge Baldwin to enter, I got my first glimpse of prosecutor Anthony Forray, a tall, thin man in a perfectly tailored brown suit. He sat at the prosecution table, hunched over some documents, a dour expression on his face. As I sat down behind the defense table to his left, Forray looked over at me. I met his gaze head-on, and he quickly turned away.

The officer who arrested me, Pottsville Police Captain Steve Durkin, sat behind Forray with some law enforcement colleagues, chuckling about the recent internet fame of Gilberton, Pennsylvania Police Chief Mark Kessler. They found it amusing that the local small-town police chief would produce a YouTube video in which he delivers a fake apology for some offensive remarks he made, then calls his critics "f**king c**k suckers" who should "Go f**k yourself" and fires off dozens of rounds from a machine gun. Hearing Durkin's group yuck it up did not reaffirm my faith in the professionalism of local law enforcement.

After a long wait, Judge Baldwin entered, looking stern but distinguished in his black robe. Unlike the magistrate who arraigned me, Baldwin had graduated from college and actually had a law degree.

The hearing lasted barely fifteen minutes. Prosecutor Forray argued that until two days ago, I had no presence on the internet, but now a search of my name produced thousands of results. He complained that the news about my case was "creating too much public sympathy for the defendant and tainting the jury pool." Though it certainly would have helped me if I could have continued talking to the media, my attorneys didn't have much legal basis for resisting the prosecution's request.

Judge Baldwin declared, "This case will not be tried in the press," and granted the gag order, covering the prosecution, my lawyer, and me. But the judge's order would only do so much to help the prosecution keep a lid on publicity about the case. It did not apply to my husband, or to Compassion and Choices, and, thanks to the First Amendment, it most certainly did not cover the media. My supporters would still be free to talk about my side of the case. The media could continue with generally sympathetic coverage.

While I wasn't happy about being personally silenced, I have to admit the gag order was fair—unlike the preliminary hearing that awaited me in Magisterial District Court 21-3-07, with restaurant-owner-turned-judge James Reiley presiding.

My lawyer and I hustled over to Magistrate Reiley's court, which was still in the same dumpy storefront where I'd been arraigned months ago. Several television news vans sat outside. Despite the gag order, my case would be big news that day.

The drab waiting area was packed with people, including many close and extended family members, my friends, and even Mom's friends.

I recognized a female television reporter from Philadelphia, but I had to wave off her questions, citing the new gag order. I also noticed two unfamiliar women glowering at me from the side of the room. I soon found out why they were glowering—they were prosecution witnesses from Hospice of Central Pennsylvania.

The hearing was held in the same cramped, dreary, windowless room as my arraignment, with the same worn brown carpet and cardboard boxes piled everywhere—quite the contrast to the stately and dignified proceeding at the Schuylkill County Courthouse. Here, at the front door of Pennsylvania's criminal justice system, defendants enter a grim, low-rent environment that sets the tone for the rudimentary legal proceedings to come.

I had to bring in my own court stenographer at a cost of $552; otherwise, the only official documentation of the hearing would be the magistrate's potentially unreliable handwritten notes. It was a hot day in August, and the room was packed with media and spectators. The room's noisy air conditioner was running at full blast. With no microphones or sound system, it was nearly impossible for anyone in the audience to hear what was said. Magistrate Reiley would soon demonstrate he either didn't understand, or simply shrugged off, the legal issues involved with the prosecution's use of leading questions and hearsay testimony.

Before we'd entered, Fanelli prepared me for the day's outcome: "I want you to know that there is zero chance that your case will be dismissed today." In Pennsylvania, all the prosecution has to do in the preliminary hearing is make a prima facie case to support the charges. It's a low bar, one the prosecution seldom fails to clear, and the prosecution possessed a distinct advantage: They were not required to turn over my father's hospice and medical records—vitally important evidence—until after the preliminary hearing. Our best hope was to establish grounds for a counterattack later in the process.

During the four-hour hearing, prosecutor Forray built his case on a shaky foundation of speculation and falsehoods.

The hospice, the police, and prosecution had all jumped to the conclusion that, because my father had taken a large dose of morphine, it must have been a suicide attempt.

But as this hearing would show, no one knew how much he took—not my father, not me, not the hospice, not the police, and not the prosecutor. The authorities simply took for granted that my father thought the amount of morphine remaining in the tiny one-ounce vial was enough to do the job for someone who (allegedly) wanted to kill himself. There was no forensic evidence that would have provided any estimate of how much morphine he'd taken.

The prosecution offered absolutely no first-hand evidence indicating that my father wanted to hasten his impending death. To show this was a "suicide attempt," the best the prosecution could do was to offer second- or third-hand accounts by people who mistakenly interpreted what I told them about my father's end-of-life wishes. Even then, hospice nurse Barbara Cattermole, first on the scene that fateful day, admitted to the court that I'd never said my father wanted to kill himself.

The entire foundation of this "assisted suicide" case—the claim that there was in fact a suicide attempt—relied on what's known in the law as hearsay, an unreliable type of evidence that is typically barred from use in court unless special conditions apply. Four different times, my attorneys objected to hearsay testimony, and four times Magistrate Reiley overruled them.

During the hearing, the prosecution tried to portray me as my father's drug courier, obtaining what he needed to try to kill himself:

> PROSECUTOR FORRAY: *"When Mr. Yourshaw started hospice in 2013, he was not on morphine; is that correct?"*
>
> BARBARA WOODS, HOSPICE DIRECTOR OF CLINICAL SERVICES: *"Correct."*
>
> FORRAY: *"Are you aware of what caused him or who requested that he be given morphine?"*
>
> WOODS: *"His daughter Barbara called into the office requesting that he be ordered morphine."*[1]

1. Transcript of Preliminary Hearing at 45, *Commonw. of Pa. v. Mancini*, CR-050-13, (Magis. Ct. Aug. 1, 2013).

While that was true, when we finally got my father's hospice records, we would discover stunning evidence that cast my phone call in a totally different light. But even with what the court was told that day, my request was a legitimate, perfectly legal attempt to obtain better pain relief for my father. If my intentions had been out of proper medical bounds, the doctor who wrote the morphine prescription for him would have refused the request.

Prosecutor Forray also wanted to plant the idea that I was trying to get my father a particularly high dose of morphine, presumably so he could more easily kill himself. His witness on this point was nurse Deborah Hornberger, the hospice team leader who handled my call about getting my father more effective pain relief.

FORRAY: *"When you were discussing with her morphine and potentially the amount of morphine that he could be given at any given time, was there, at least initially, a difference in opinions as to how much he should be getting?"*

HORNBERGER: *"Yes, there was."*

FORRAY: *"Can you explain that?"*

HORNBERGER: *"Yes. She asked for a higher amount. I know it was at least 5 milligrams at a time and I said because he was opioid naïve that I would consider talking to the physician and recommending a 2.5 milligram dose, but that I did not feel that it was recommended to go above 2.5 milligrams."*[2]

In reality, I never asked for a specific dose of morphine. Later, I'd learn that Hornberger's own notes in the hospice record contradicted the prosecution's contention that I was after a large morphine dose: "Contacted by daughter requesting a low dose morphine order because her dad is c/o [complaining of] pain all over."[3]

Even if I'd specifically asked for a five-milligram dose, it was hardly proof of nefarious intent. When Stephen Goldfine, chief medical officer

2. *Id.* at 100.
3. 2013 Hospice of Central Pennsylvania Record of Joseph Yourshaw, p. 66.

for Samaritan Hospice in South Jersey, was later asked by a journalist about my case, he said, "Even for an opiate-naïve patient, a 5-milligram dose is reasonable and common."[4]

Most outrageous of all, I was accused of being so eager to see my father finished off that I allegedly asked for even more morphine after the hospice nurse arrived.

"I asked her how much [morphine] she had given him," nurse Barbara Cattermole testified about me, "and she said she gave him the whole bottle. I was trying to figure out how much that was. I asked if he was dead, and she said no. . . . She asked if I could get more morphine. I told her I could not do that."[5]

"Holy crap, I am screwed," I thought when I heard that. Her claim that I asked for more morphine was a bald-face lie, but it landed with all the authority of first-hand testimony delivered under oath. We had no compelling way to refute her fabricated testimony. It was her word against mine. In his closing statement to Magistrate Reiley, prosecutor Forray reiterated Cattermole's damning accusation, claiming that because Dad hadn't died, I was after more morphine "to do the trick."[6]

That accusation was just one of many sickening blows I suffered during the hearing. Cattermole delivered another when she testified that she feared for her safety.

"I was hoping the three of us [she, my father, and me] got out of there alive, because I was worried," she testified.[7] I had now morphed into a possible mass murderer! Though Cattermole quickly backtracked on that point, admitting that she did not tell her supervisors, police, or EMTs that she feared personal harm[8], it didn't undo the shock she'd inflicted on me.

Later, I was shocked yet again to hear police captain Steve Durkin blatantly lie about what I'd told him.

---

4. http://articles.philly.com/2014-01-16/news/46228584_1_hospice-nurse-barbara-mancini-prescribed-morphine.

5. Transcript of Preliminary Hearing at 57-58, *Commonw. of Pa. v. Mancini*, CR-050-13, (Magis. Ct. Aug. 1, 2013).

6. *Id.* at 152.

7. *Id.* at 60.

8. *Id.* at 95.

PROSECUTOR FORRAY: *"Did she [defendant Mancini] explain what she had done or what role she had played in this?"*
CAPTAIN DURKIN: *"Yes, she said several times that she gave him the morphine so he could die."*[9]

Once again, my legal team had no compelling way to attack this damning but false testimony. It was my word against his.

Having to sit through these lies and assaults on my character was like being caught in an abusive interrogation scene from a bad movie. It was as if I was tied to a chair, defenseless, so that someone could punch me in the gut . . . again . . . and again . . . and again.

But there was one point where the prosecution's witness spun such a contorted tale of what happened that I had to laugh to myself.

Hospice nurse Cattermole was asked about why she had given my father the Reiki treatment. At first, she accurately reported what she'd told me.

DEFENSE ATTORNEY: *"You were trying to help him [my father] pass, right? Isn't that what you told Barbara?"*
CATTERMOLE: *"Yes, I did tell Barbara."*[10]

But then she immediately reversed herself, saying of the Reiki treatment, "A chakra spread is used for anyone in transition of anything. It doesn't have to be a dying person. . . . It doesn't help anybody pass." The real reason she gave my father a Reiki treatment, Cattermole testified, was to help "calm" me, because I was supposedly so agitated right from the start. In fact, I'd watched peacefully while she did the Reiki for my father.

Cattermole told the court that while doing the Reiki, she was also assessing my father's condition, checking his breathing and assessing the color and temperature of my father's hands and feet. In fact, his stocking feet were under bed covers the whole time.

9. *Id.* at 126.
10. *Id.* at 83.

Having watched her do the Reiki treatment, I knew it took Cattermole several minutes, but that's not what she said during cross-examination by my attorney:

> DEFENSE ATTORNEY: *"Well, this Reiki treatment—"*
> CATTERMOLE: *"Takes three seconds."*
> DEFENSE ATTORNEY: *"Only three seconds?"*
> CATTERMOLE: *"Yeah, I can do it to you real quick. Maybe five. I didn't even do the whole thing. But the whole time I'm watching—"*
> DEFENSE ATTORNEY: *"So, you did this Reiki to him prior to calling your supervisor; is that correct?"*
> CATTERMOLE: *"Correct, I was assessing the patient. His respirations were 16. He wasn't in trouble of not breathing at that point, and Barbara was between me and the door and I needed to get to the door."*[11]

That's when I had to stifle a laugh. Cattermole was claiming that she did a full physical assessment of my dad while performing Reiki, touching and observing his hands and feet, waving her hands over the seven chakras of his body, counting his respiratory rate, and offering comfort to me, all in three to five seconds, while plotting how to get safely get out the door.

Now that's a courtroom re-enactment I'd like to see.

The preliminary hearing did provide one moment of TV-show type drama. It came when my attorney cross-examined Barbara Woods, the hospice supervisor who insisted my father had to go to the hospital for a morphine "overdose."

My attorney asked, "You're aware that during the hospitalization he was given morphine?"[12]

11. *Id.* at 85.
12. *Id.* at 44.

Hearing that, prosecutor Forray snapped his head up, quickly looked around, then shuffled frantically through the files in front of him. Everyone sitting in the front row saw his stunned reaction, and several mentioned it to me after the hearing.

Forray was obviously ignorant of this key fact—that the hospital had given my father morphine shortly before his death. That morphine dose completely undermined the fundamental premise of his case.

To reinforce the claim that this was an attempted suicide, orchestrated by me, Forray relied on the (flawed) autopsy's finding that my father's death was due to "morphine toxicity," somehow resulting from a dose he took nearly five days earlier. But the short-acting morphine he took would have been metabolized out of his bloodstream. The morphine in my father at his death came from a dose delivered at the hospital.

Seen in this light, morphine in his body reflected a compassionate attempt to give relief to dying patient. Morphine was no longer just a potentially fatal drug that "proved" there had been a suicide attempt.

Later in the hearing, Captain Durkin admitted that he also didn't know the hospital had given my father morphine. It was a basic fact he would have discovered if he'd checked the hospital records. Unlike Durkin, I didn't yet have access to those records, but I knew what had happened, because I was there when the hospital nurse gave the morphine to him.

However, reading my dad's hospital record was apparently too much trouble for the officer. "It's a pretty thick thing," Durkin testified. And even if he had read through it, he said, "I don't understand whether it [a hospital-administered dose of morphine] would be a good thing or a bad thing. I'm not a doctor."

"As a policeman," Durkin tried to explain, "I'm looking for cause of death to be listed as morphine toxicity."[13] He found it in the autopsy, so that was that—case closed. No need to look at the hospital records that might have confirmed—or undercut—his case.

---

13. *Id.* at 137-138.

Though we did not yet have access to critical medical record evidence, my attorneys exposed some key flaws in the prosecution's case. They flagged several of the witnesses' key assertions as hearsay. They got the prosecution's witnesses to admit that I had merely handed my father the vial of morphine; he took the morphine himself. (So much for the claim, slipped to Magistrate Reiley outside of proper court proceedings, that I had forced the morphine down my father's throat.) The court record would show that I never told my father to drink all the morphine. It would show that I never said that my father wanted to kill himself. It would show that nobody knew how much morphine my father took, and however much he took, he was breathing normally when the hospice nurse evaluated him.

Nonetheless, as Fanelli predicted, Magistrate Reiley immediately bound my case over for trial. Thankfully, I was still free on bond and able to aid in my own defense.

As we all stood up to leave, I could see anger and despair on the faces of my supporters. The prosecution's witnesses were discreetly led out a back exit, but I had to face a throng of reporters lobbing questions at me, thrusting their microphones into my face while TV cameras zoomed in on me. The press horde followed us for about a block, but we were bound by court order not to talk, so they returned to the crowd of my supporters still milling about on the sidewalk. There, the reporters gathered sympathetic reactions that would help define the tone of that day's news coverage.

Leaving behind the storefront courtroom, with its worn carpet, stacks of file boxes, noisy air conditioner, and a magistrate with only skeletal training in the law, I now understood how easily an innocent person could be falsely accused. I had just come face-to-face with the harsh reality of criminal justice in the United States.

But now that the preliminary hearing was over, I would get full access to my father's hospice and hospital records—documents that would eventually help tear the prosecution's case apart.

CHAPTER 8

Discovery

Wrongful convictions occur every month in every state in this country, and the reasons are all varied and all the same—bad police work, junk science, faulty eyewitness identifications, bad defense lawyers, lazy prosecutors, arrogant prosecutors.

—John Grisham

OUR INVESTIGATION INTO the newly available records started with a drive to Harrisburg, where Hospice of Central Pennsylvania has its home office. While Fanelli waited to receive the records from the prosecutor, he advised me we could get them more quickly ourselves if Mom—the surviving spouse—requested them directly from the hospice. I had no idea that the trip with Mom and my husband, Joe, would so quickly bear fruit.

Because my relations with the hospice were antagonistic—three of its employees were key witnesses who testified against me—my attorney instructed me to have no dealings with any of the staff. So, while Mom and Joe went in to collect the records she'd requested, I stayed in the car, sipped on some tea, and tried to distract myself by surfing through the local radio channels. I wondered how the hospice staff would treat Mom's request. Would they be ashamed, because their care for my father was so poor? Would they be hostile, because all the media attention to my case brought them bad publicity? Would they be icy and distant, treating her as the mother of a dragon lady daughter who'd plotted to help her father attempt suicide?

After twenty minutes, Mom and Joe emerged with the records in hand. Mom said the hospice employees were cordial—they showed no surprise at seeing her, and they offered her and Joe coffee and a place to sit while they retrieved the records.

As I drove home, Joe leafed through the files. Within two minutes he yelled, "Look at this! Dad was ordered to have morphine right away, the second time he started hospice!"

"What?!" I shouted.

"The order says 'for moderate to severe pain, 5-10 mg of morphine every 2–4 hours as needed, may titrate [increase] one to two times the base dose.' It's right here—dated January 18!"

"Whoa! I cannot believe this!" I cried.

So much for the prosecution's attempt to finger me as the only reason Dad was provided morphine during his second hospice enrollment. His doctor had prescribed it for him from day one. When hospice team leader Deborah Hornberger argued with me and said that morphine wasn't appropriate for Dad, she was contradicting medical orders provided by his physician. When Hornberger then relented and arranged for Dad to get morphine, she imposed her own judgment and made sure it was a much smaller dose than his doctor originally ordered—a dose too small to give him the pain relief he needed.

"Dammit!" I yelled. "What is wrong with these people?"

Joe read off more of the medicine list and I barked, "Stop! I won't be able to drive home listening to this! Let's get home safely and then we can read the records."

The morphine order for Dad was placed near the front of his hospice chart. For anyone even casually leafing through his chart, it would have been hard to miss. The order was also part of his electronic health record; there was a printout of it in his file. That meant the order was available to anyone who had computer access to my father's records—in other words, the entire hospice team. They all knew, or should have known, that my father was to have received morphine. The orders also said, "Patient may self-administer medications." That's exactly what he did after I handed him the morphine.

Reading that part of the file made me doubly angry. I remembered how, at the preliminary hearing, hospice clinical director Barbara Woods said, "We have to function within the physician orders."[1] But here was clear documentary evidence that Dad's "physician orders" included morphine, and the hospice did not provide it until I called.

When Woods testified in court, she suggested the hospice was reluctant to second-guess the patient's doctor. "We do not try to give orders or medications beyond what the doctor has recommended and ordered,"[2] she said. But in managing Dad's pain, the hospice proved all too willing to do a lot less than "what the doctor has recommended and ordered." It withheld the medicines prescribed by Dad's doctor. It failed to let us know that those medicines had been prescribed and then withheld. When I finally called the hospice to get pain medicine for Dad, the hospice resisted and argued for continuing to withhold morphine, even though his doctor had initially ordered it. And when the hospice relented and supplied the morphine, it was far less than half the dose his doctor had initially prescribed.

During my preliminary hearing, Prosecutor Forray had dramatically pointed at me and told the magistrate, "Look at the facts as we have them in this particular case. There was no morphine in the home. Who was responsible for requesting the morphine to be in the home? The defendant. She was insistent that it be morphine."[3]

Yeah, I was "insistent that it be morphine." Turns out I was simply insisting that the hospice supply the medicine Dad had already been prescribed.

---

1. Transcript of Preliminary Hearing at 21, *Commw. of Pa. v. Mancini*, CR-050-13, (Magis. Ct. Aug. 1, 2013.

2. *Id.* at 42.

3. *Id.* at 151.

In the court of public opinion, the prosecution continued to lose ground. News coverage of the preliminary hearing had spread rapidly, far beyond Pottsville and Philadelphia. Articles appeared on internet news sites across the United States and in places as far away as Britain, Israel, South Africa, Japan, Australia, and Italy. It was a story with global reach, because anyone with access to modern medicine could imagine someday confronting agonizing end-of-life choices—and wonder whether they or their loved ones might face the same kind of legal persecution.

The coverage prompted a torrent of commentary, all of it criticizing the prosecution for pursuing a heartless, legally dubious case. It was encouraging to read that my family and I were not the only ones who felt that an appalling injustice was occurring.

In the *New York Times*, columnist Frank Bruni noted that my father was near death, and that the evidence of any "crime" was weak, so much so that even "a leading opponent of assisted suicide [was] scratching his head about the way the case is being handled."

"It would have been easy for prosecutors to walk away; that sort of thing happens all the time," Bruni wrote. Their decision to file charges, "suggests how conflicted, inconsistent, and bullheaded we Americans can be when it comes to the very private, very intimate business of dying." He questioned how, "in an era of severely limited government resources, the dedication of time and money to this case made any sense."[4]

An editorial in the *Philadelphia Daily News* said what I'd felt from the day of my arrest: "A caring daughter who is also a nurse is being treated like she's a criminal and a threat to society. Her life is in a state of traumatic limbo. . . . It's indecent. It's infuriating."[5]

Nick Vadala, in *Philadelphia Magazine*, called the case "a witch hunt," made possible by ambiguous and outdated laws. He said those laws persist because legislators are "profoundly disturbed by the concept of death itself" and refuse to recognize the heart-wrenching dilemmas that terminally ill patients and their loved ones face.[6]

4. http://www.nytimes.com/2013/08/11/opinion/sunday/bruni-fatal-mercies.html?_r=0.
5. http://articles.philly.com/2013-08-14/news/41378682_1_hospice-nurse-caseleach.
6. http://www.phillymag.com/news/2013/08/02/pennsylvania-death-with-dignity-assisted-suicide-law/.

One of my most avid defenders was columnist Paul Carpenter, with the *Allentown Morning Call.* "A 93-year-old man was dying and was in terrible agony from multiple problems, although his mind was sharp enough to feel them all," he wrote, but "the power structure wanted to keep him that way indefinitely."[7]

Some commentaries didn't get the facts perfectly straight, but they were good on the essentials. David Casarett, a hospice doctor in Philadelphia, misunderstood the charge against me. It was the felony of assisting an attempted suicide, not murder—but his piece in the *Huffington Post* hit the absurdity of the case and the dangers it posed. "Barbara Mancini is being charged for . . . what, exactly? For handing her dying father a bottle of pills that were appropriately prescribed and legally obtained? For being a good caregiver? For being a dutiful daughter?"

"Many of my patients already feel that they're a burden to their families," Casarett wrote. "They're worried about the stress that their families are under. Now, apparently, they need to worry that their husbands and wives and daughters will end up facing murder [*sic*] charges."[8]

I started receiving letters of support and encouragement, not only from people I knew, but also from relatives I had lost touch with and people I'd never even met. My mother, who had lived in Pottsville almost her entire life, was showered with overwhelming support and sympathy from friends, neighbors, acquaintances, and fellow church members. My siblings' friends and work colleagues also spoke out in solidarity. After months of feeling isolated and trapped in this nightmare, I was deeply touched and grateful.

Digging deeper into the hospice records, I found the critical point at which my father was pushed onto the painful path that ended with an agonizing, medically intensive death.

That path started when nurse Barbara Cattermole assessed Dad for his second hospice admission. In her write-up, she noted that his doctor

7. www.call.com/news/local/carpenter/mc-pc-aiding-suicide-charge-20130810,0,2101320.column.
8. http://www.huffingtonpost.com/david-casarett-md/caring-daughter-or-murder_b_3681717.html.

had in fact prescribed him pain medicine, including morphine. However, she also wrote that Dad refused these medications, so she did not provide them.

Neither Mom nor I were present when Cattermole interviewed Dad. It is possible that Dad told her he didn't want *any* medicine, but he was always clear to us: He did not want any medicine *if he thought it would prolong his life.* He was hard of hearing, so I don't know if he understood that the prescription medicines offered by the hospice were intended to make him comfortable. He needn't have worried that they would prolong his suffering.

And that suffering was obvious. Every time I spoke to Dad, he told me he was in pain. To treat it, I knew he was taking Tylenol and ibuprofen (and lots of it). Cattermole recognized it too—her notes state that Dad complained of chest pain all the time.

But Cattermole never informed Mom or me that she decided to withhold the prescribed pain medicines, so we never had a chance to clear up any misunderstanding Dad may have had. Failing to involve us—Dad's caregivers—in a discussion about this profound decision affecting his end-of-life care was an inexcusable failure on the hospice's part.

Other entries in the hospice record had me puzzled. Several different nurses who saw my father at home noted that he had weakness and fatigue, that he was unsteady in walking, and that he became winded with minimal exertion. Yet, they frequently wrote that he "expressed relief of his weakness and fatigue 75% of the time or greater. Goal met with ongoing IDT [interdisciplinary team] actions."

There is only one way that claim could have been true: If by "relief of his weakness and fatigue," the hospice meant the time he spent sleeping. He was so fatigued that he slept sixteen to eighteen hours a day. In the six to eight hours a day he spent awake, his weakness and fatigue were unabated. Apparently, the hospice didn't want to be honest and admit there wasn't much it could do about his "weakness and fatigue" with "ongoing IDT actions." He was a dying man, steadily growing weaker and more fatigued. But the hospice had to make it look as if it was delivering care that was worth the $153 a day it collected for serving Dad. In the medical world, there is a term for that kind of duplicitous record-keeping. It's called "false charting."

As we sorted through the records now available to us, Compassion and Choices was hard at work on a different front. It began an online campaign urging people to demand that Pennsylvania Attorney General Kathleen Kane cease this "aggressive criminal prosecution." The public response was overwhelming. So many sympathizers contacted the Office of the Attorney General's website that it crashed several times.

The attorney general's office clearly had not anticipated this kind of blowback. A few days after the preliminary hearing, as critical articles continued to spread, Fred Fanelli received an unusual call from Deputy AG Forray: Could Fanelli please tell Compassion and Choices to stop talking about my case? Not only did the AG's website crash, the office was getting so many protest calls that the agency's switchboard couldn't handle them all. Doing his best to disguise his delight, Fanelli informed Forray, "I have no control over what Compassion and Choices talks about."

The media was calling the attorney general's office too. But because of the gag order, which the prosecution itself had requested, the AG could not explain or defend the decision to prosecute me.

At election time, prosecutors love to remind voters about how they are making communities safer by locking up criminals. Every election season, prosecutors use the same refrain: We are "tough on crime" and we can boast high conviction rates. Now the Pottsville police and the Pennsylvania attorney general were being asked to explain how arresting and prosecuting a loving caregiver to her dying father was making anyone safe. In fact, they were making people feel less safe. Everyone caring for a terminally ill person now had reason to worry about being charged with a crime.

I would understand some kind of investigation to rule out elder abuse, which is a serious problem in the United States. But any such investigation would have shown that I had a close and loving relationship with both of my parents, and I did not profit in any way from my father's death.

The prosecution knew it was losing the overwhelming advantages it enjoys over almost every defendant. Gone was the swagger prosecutor Forray had shown early on, when he'd threatened that there would be zero chance of a plea bargain if my defense team insisted on grilling his witnesses at the preliminary hearing.

Facing the uncontrollable outbreak of hostile publicity, Forray called my attorney three times to discuss a plea bargain. Each time, my response was clear: No deal. Either drop the charge against me or I would go to trial. I'd done nothing wrong and was not going to say otherwise, even if it would save me thousands of dollars in legal fees. But the attorney general's office refused to admit that bringing the case was a mistake.

Perhaps Attorney General Kathleen Kane and her staff feared they would be perceived as "giving in" to public pressure. But Kane refused to recognize that the entire case was based on a tragic misunderstanding of a stressful encounter and misinformation from the hospice and police.

Nonetheless, the winds of my misfortune had begun to shift in ways that were favorable to me. Hospice records contradicted many things the hospice witnesses said in their sworn testimony at my preliminary hearing, so my lawyer would be able to discredit the witnesses at trial. I also now had access to the hospital, autopsy, and toxicology reports. They all indicated that law enforcement based the case almost entirely on hospice witness statements, without bothering to cross-check the evidence in the medical records. Exposing that sloppy investigative work would help us argue that the case never should have been brought.

The torment of this ordeal still kept me awake at night. But I found some solace knowing that the chorus of outrage over the case was growing; public sympathy was clearly on my side.

The balance of power in the case had flipped. It was time to counterattack.

CHAPTER 9

Counterattack

Justice will not be served until those who are unaffected are as outraged as those who are.

—Benjamin Franklin

KNOWING THAT WHAT we found in the records would let us go on the offensive was a candle of hope in the darkness. The growing chorus of public support helped, too, but I was still a boiling cauldron of worry, anxiety, fear, anger, disbelief, outrage, and mistrust verging on paranoia.

When I would visit my mom in Pottsville, we would go out together on errands. Inevitably, she would meet someone she knew, and she would want to introduce me. I'd rather have been locked alone in a cave for a week than forced to meet a complete stranger.

One time that she drew me over to meet someone, I really lost it. I yelled at the top of my voice, "Don't EVER—EVER!—pull me over and introduce me to anybody EVER AGAIN!" I'd never acted like that around her before.

After Dad died, I didn't visit Mom as much as either of us would have liked. I lived a hundred miles away, and I spent much of my time and energy researching my defense and trying to maintain my sanity. On one visit to Pottsville, she told me, as she often did, "I wish I saw more of you." She didn't realize it, but that time, her heartfelt request lit a match that set off an explosion.

"How much do you want me to come up here?" I shouted. "What do you feel is often enough?"

Taken aback, she meekly replied, "Oh . . . once a week."

I thought: Once a week?! "WELL FORGET IT!" I roared. For me to even go up there at all was painful. Simply crossing the boundary into Schuylkill County brought back every emotion and negative thought. Sometimes, I'd just start to cry. And for her to tell me I wasn't coming up enough . . . that was just too much.

At home, I spent a lot of time on the internet, researching similar cases and seeking ideas to exploit the flaws in the shoddy investigation used to prosecute me. Joe probably felt neglected, and sometimes when he'd approach me at the computer, I'd snap at him. My two daughters knew it was generally best to steer clear of Mom. They spent a lot of time holed up in their rooms. The best we could do to maintain a semblance of normal family routines was to eat dinner together.

My brother, Jim, whom I love and always got along well with, was another undeserving target of my fury. One time I was on the phone with him, telling him that because he lives near Mom, he really needs to be there for her and do more to support her. He was a little dismissive, hemming and hawing a bit, and I exploded at him.

"The only thing keeping me from putting a gun in my mouth and pulling the trigger is knowing how it would hurt Mom and Joe and the kids!" Then I dropped a string of F-bombs on him.

I'd never acted like that before. What I said was the truth, though. It would have been much easier, and much less painful, if I'd just done myself in. It was a testament to my love for my husband, my children, and my mother that I didn't do it. It's the only reason I didn't. I knew it would hurt them a lot more.

I found myself incapable of engaging in or even listening to the small talk that people share during normal conversations. It seemed absurd to pretend to act normally when nothing about my life was normal. I avoided going places where I might be recognized, and I dreaded it when people asked me how I was doing. If I didn't know them well, I'd shake my head and not say anything and hope they'd change the subject. To those I knew better, I'd say "I'm struggling," but I was hesitant to say more, because they probably really didn't want to hear any of the intimate details.

Some people wouldn't say anything at all about my awful situation, and that was really uncomfortable. I'd automatically think, "They're judging me. They think I tried to kill my dad." My reaction made no sense, but I was not in a mental place where much of anything made sense.

I understood that many times people just did not know what to say. Probably what helped the most was hearing "I'm thinking of you and hoping this ends soon." As for the deaths of my father, father-in-law, and aunt—I tucked my grief into a remote corner of my heart, where it would remain unacknowledged for another two years.

Well-meaning relatives and friends suggested I see a mental health professional, but I dismissed that idea out-of-hand. What was the point? No anti-anxiety or antidepressant drug could end the criminal case against me or undo the brutal medical torture my father suffered before he died. I told myself, "A pill's not going to take away my distress. My distress is because of the situation I'm in. It's externally imposed. They have to right this wrong."

In my desperation to find some relief, I tried acupuncture and tai chi. Acupuncture didn't do a thing for me. As I glanced at other people on the treatment tables, relaxed and falling asleep, I'd be lying there with needles stuck in me, and I didn't feel one bit of difference. Tai chi didn't help, either. In tai chi, you're concentrating on physical movement and the position of your body. It takes your mind away from all the stressful things you're thinking about. But I was in a place where nothing was going to work until that charge was dropped. I was a volcano of stress hormones, ready to erupt at the slightest prodding, no matter how innocent or well-intentioned.

I was fortunate in that I didn't try to kill my pain with alcohol, and I didn't do any kind of drugs. The thing that helped the most was taking long daily walks with our German shepherd, Dano. My home is a few short blocks from the edge of Wissahickon Valley Park, part of the Fairmount Park system in Philadelphia. The park is a true urban gem, an oasis of forest, meadows, and streams woven into the neighborhoods of the nation's sixth-largest city. I took Dano on steep, rocky back trails where we rarely encountered any people. It was there that I felt free to vent my rage.

I'd spew F-bombs at each and every person responsible for my ordeal. I cursed them all, for what they did to my dad, to my family, and to me. While I raged, Dano was the perfect, non-judgmental listener. The first few times, he'd cock his head and look at me quizzically. Soon he learned this curious behavior from me was just a regular part of our walks, and he would simply carry on with his usual trotting and sniffing.

With each day's catharsis, I found relief, at least temporarily, from my hurt and anger and outrage. I could then focus on the wooded canvas surrounding me—the unique fragrance of damp leaves, tree bark, and dirt; the muffled sound of my footfalls over packed earthen trails; the sun peeking through the lace curtain of leaves as thin saplings craned upward toward a sliver of light in the dense foliage; the discordant rattle of cicadas rippling from one end of the woods to the other.

My attorney had been optimistic from the start that we could get the charges against me dismissed. But now we had documents that would destroy the entire foundation of the prosecution's case. We would not sit back and wait until the criminal trial to fight back in court. Instead, Fanelli filed a petition for habeas corpus in the Schuylkill County Court of Common Pleas.

A habeas corpus petition is a way to force the government to show that it has sufficient evidence for locking up a person or for pursuing a criminal charge. If the prosecution cannot do so, the court will grant the petition and dismiss the case.

Habeas corpus petitions rarely succeed in getting charges dismissed before the criminal trial. In Pennsylvania, a habeas petition that is filed before the trial essentially duplicates the protection supposedly offered by the preliminary hearing. In theory, the preliminary hearing ensures an innocent person is not locked up or dragged to trial on baseless charges. But my preliminary hearing was hopelessly tainted by false testimony, something we could now prove, thanks to the evidence we got in discovery.

In our habeas petition, Fanelli pointed out that there was no valid evidence for key elements of the supposed crime of "assisting" a "suicide." The claim that this was a suicide attempt—that my father took the morphine because he wanted to kill himself—was based on unreliable hearsay testimony that by law should have been barred. Also, there was no reliable evidence about how much morphine my father took. Therefore, his decision to consume all of what was left in the one-ounce vial could not be proof that he intended to commit suicide.

No matter how much morphine he took, Fanelli noted, my father was in pain and had the constitutional right to give himself as much morphine as he wanted to relieve his pain, even if it hastened his death. That right was recognized in 1997 by US Supreme Court rulings in the cases of *Washington v. Glucksberg* and *Vacco v. Quill.* "Ms. Mancini's involvement in the exercise of her father's constitutional right," Fanelli wrote, "cannot be a crime."

Though asserting that my father tried to take his life, the prosecution did not claim that his "suicide attempt" was successful. Fanelli reminded the court that the state conceded that my father did not die from the morphine he took. In fact, the hospital gave my father morphine to help ease his pain on the last day of his life.

Nor was there any legally valid evidence to support the claim that I was scheming to "assist" my father in committing suicide. The only evidence on that score was inadmissible hearsay testimony from witnesses who had, in the heat of the moment, jumped to false conclusions about what I said.

In any event, the prosecution failed to demonstrate that I had provided "assistance without which the suicide or attempted suicide would not have occurred," as the criminal statute requires. My father was perfectly capable of getting his own medicine and opening the vial and taking the dose, and he in fact had done so on previous occasions.

Fanelli's brief went on to argue that any anti-assisted suicide law that arguably applies to the simple caregiving act that I performed is unconstitutional. Pennsylvania's statute does not define the crucial terms "causing," "aiding," or "soliciting," nor does it give examples of what would be covered by the law. Because the law is so vague, he argued, it is impossible to know how to obey it. Innocent people (like me) are left worrying that their perfectly legal behavior will be prosecuted. (It's a well-settled legal principle that to be constitutional and enforceable, a law must give people fair warning about what behavior or action will violate the law.[1])

Fanelli also mentioned some details that drove home the very real human suffering at the center of the case—suffering that my father had carefully tried to avoid. My father had executed an advance directive making clear that he did not want life-prolonging interventions. He was adamant that he wanted to die at home. Despite this, the hospice called 911 and had him taken to the hospital. He died five days later, after twice receiving morphine reversal drugs, which left him in brutal pain. I'm not sure those details carried any weight on the legal questions in the case, but perhaps they helped build sympathy in the mind of the judge reviewing the petition.

Our habeas corpus petition got support from two patients' rights organizations—Compassion and Choices and a noncommercial resource for health-care professionals and their patients called Pain Treatment Topics. In an amicus curiae (or friend of the court) brief, the groups noted that the supposedly criminal act was simply "a family member handing pain medicine to a dying hospice patient." Allowing the charge to stand would mean that those who care for a dying family member "will have reason to fear that their provision of care could cost them their liberty," the brief said. "This would be tragic for dying patients nationwide."[2]

1. https://www.law.cornell.edu/wex/vagueness_doctrine.

2. Brief Amicus Curiae of Compassion and Choices and Pain Treatment Topics in Support of Defendant's Motion for Habeas Corpus at 6, *Commw. of Pa. v. Mancini*, No. CR-1305-2013.

The groups also reminded the court of the 1997 US Supreme Court's ruling in the Glucksberg case. As Justice Sandra Day O'Connor wrote in her concurring opinion, "[A] patient who is suffering from a terminal illness and who is experiencing great pain has no legal barriers to obtaining medication, from qualified physicians, to alleviate that suffering, even to the point of causing unconsciousness and hastening death."[3]

Media commentaries continued to criticize the decision to prosecute me. Gwen Fitzgerald wrote in *USA Today*, "Joe Yourshaw was very old and terminally ill. He had end-stage diabetes, heart and kidney failure, and arthritis. He died just short of his 94th birthday. Where is the public interest in constructing a criminal case from this scenario?"

"Millions of families across America are facing end-of-life decisions every day, as we baby boomers care for our parents," Fitzgerald wrote. "Do the 75 million-plus boomers need to fear the long arm of government literally reaching into our living rooms to seize authority for our medical decisions?"[4]

Matthew Major asked his readers in the *Public Opinion* [Chambersburg, PA], "Do we really want cops and medical personnel arbitrarily making decisions that overrule our express wishes? . . . Why didn't state Attorney General Kathleen Kane back slowly away from this one? . . . When officials cast end-of-life issues through a pro-life prism for political gain, we start treading on unholy ground."[5]

And concern about my prosecution was being raised by an unlikely source—the disability-rights group Not Dead Yet, which stridently opposes medical aid-in-dying. "Never mind public sentiment," said Stephen Drake, a spokesperson, "you've got big evidentiary problems . . . all she did was hand her father his own prescription medication, which was meant for pain relief, and he was entitled to take what he wanted."[6]

---

3. *Washington v. Glucksberg*, 521 U.S. 702,737 (1997).

4. http://www.usatoday.com/story/opinion/2013/08/20/assisted-suicide-medicine-baby-boomers-health-care-column/2650461/.

5. *Public Opinion* News Editorial, August 23, 2013.

6. http://articles.philly.com/2013-10-01/news/42539828_1_morphine-steve-durkin-hospice-nurse.

The gag order prevented me from talking about my case, but it didn't prevent my husband from standing up for me in the media. "How do you put into words how someone you love is being so wronged? And has been so unfairly and unjustly prosecuted and persecuted by the state Attorney General's Office?" Joe told the *Philadelphia Inquirer*.[7]

Joe continued to be my best character witness, as in this sympathetic account from the Associated Press:

> Barbara Mancini had urged her father to seek medical care at critical times in his life, when Yourshaw was reluctant to do so. That led him to be diagnosed with diabetes and, later, a stroke, Joe Mancini said. She also helped care for a sister and other family members. . . . [Her husband said,] "Barb did all of these loving things for her parents and sister despite living nearly 100 miles away, despite having two daughters to raise, despite working a demanding job, and despite everything that involves being a loving wife. Barb did all she did out of love and devotion."[8]

To this day, I know how lucky I am to have a spouse who stood by me through such an ordeal. The strain on all of us was so intense, it easily could have cracked our marriage apart. Instead, it drew us closer together, which is a testament to his good character and the strong commitment we made to each other.

I was also greatly moved by the unsolicited offers of many people—friends, neighbors, and co-workers—to testify in court for me, should I need them. I don't know how I could have survived without the wonderful support I received.

However, by this point, my legal fees, which had reached $65,000 before I hired Fanelli for my defense, now topped $100,000. Joe and I had always been careful not to live beyond our means. But this was a huge amount of money for us. My income was gone. I had drained my entire savings account. We were now borrowing money to pay my legal

7. Ibid. (same as note 5).
8. http://triblive.com/state/pennsylvania/4730199-74/mancini-morphine-case.

fees. We had a house with monthly expenses, and our older daughter was in her first year of college. Joe had to work many overtime shifts in his job as a paramedic to cover my loss of income. Along with the unrelenting stress of living a nightmare, I wondered if we would survive it all.

At Schuylkill County Court of Common Pleas, our case was assigned to Judge Jacqueline Russell. While she had a reputation for being a strict jurist who is hard on criminals, Fanelli had high regard for her as fair-minded. Judge Russell set a hearing for the habeas corpus motion on October 10, 2013, at the county courthouse in Pottsville.

This time, with all the relevant evidence available to us, we would be fighting on a level playing field, in front of judge with a law degree—not a former restaurant owner. It would be a hearing with a real-life Perry Mason moment, when the lead prosecutor was forced to make an admission that would ultimately sink his case.

CHAPTER 10

"What is the evidence?"

As long as justice and injustice have not terminated their ever-renewing fight for ascendancy in the affairs of mankind, human beings must be willing, when need is, to do battle for the one against the other.

—John Stuart Mill

AS I DROVE into a space in the back lot of the Schuylkill County courthouse on October 10, 2013, television camera crews massed near the entrance. They were filming my supporters, who were standing nearby, holding large pictures of Dad and me with signs that read "Let Joe RIP"; "Stop Wasting Taxpayer $!"; "We Support Barbara!"; "Prosecuting Barbara ≠ Justice!" and "Dismiss This Joke!"

When the media gaggle noticed I'd arrived for the court hearing on my habeas corpus motion, they quickly pivoted and trailed Mom and me as we walked hand-in-hand into the courthouse, our heads held high. Reporters shouted questions at me, but of course, I could not respond; I was still bound by the gag order.

The courthouse security screeners were considerate and kind to us. Though it seems like a small detail, and it didn't mean they felt any particular sympathy for my cause, their kindness mattered a great deal to me. It felt as if I were going into a place where justice might actually be dispensed.

Mom and I climbed the marble steps up to Courtroom 2, where Judge Jacqueline Russell would preside. The hallway was lined with more of my supporters sitting on benches and milling about as we all waited for the courtroom doors to open.

Journalist Brad Bumsted, from the *Pittsburgh Tribune* newspaper, introduced himself and started to ask some questions. I politely informed him I couldn't respond because of the gag order. Not to be deterred, he asked if we could talk about something else, such as the weather. I felt like a trap was being laid and I might unwittingly violate the gag order. Instead, I told him how I had tripped over Dano the day before while playing ball with him and landed flat on my face, which explained why I had a swollen and lacerated upper lip. At that, luckily, Bumsted seemed to lose interest.

Joe listened as another journalist asked my younger daughter, who had just turned sixteen, how she was doing. She lamented, "I'm tired of being sad all the time, and I'm tired of seeing my mom and dad so sad all the time." It broke Joe's heart to hear her say that.

Just before the hearing was due to start, my attorney confidently strode down the corridor to Courtroom 2, a striped umbrella in one hand and a bulging brief case in the other. He was smartly dressed in a dark suit accented by a dotted tie. Though his face was rather boyish, his wire-rimmed glasses and short gray hair gave him an air of experience and authority.

When the massive wooden courtroom doors opened, my family, supporters, and the media packed the courtroom. Judge Russell opened the proceeding and Deputy Attorney General Forray began by recapping testimony from the preliminary hearing. Our legal brief had attacked much of that testimony as complete hearsay, with no independent corroboration that any crime was committed. Today, we also had records to prove that some of the key testimony Forray would cite was false. However, there was no guarantee that the judge would allow us to introduce this newly discovered evidence.

Early on, we got a hopeful sign that Judge Russell was no pushover for the prosecution. It came when Forray criticized our side for raising the

US Supreme Court decisions in the 1997 *Glucksberg* and *Quill* cases. He delivered a long explanation of what the court meant by those decisions, which seemed to rub Judge Russell the wrong way. "Counsel, I don't really need you to tell me what the Supreme Court said in opinions," she said. "I'm capable of reading and understanding the opinions."[1]

As Fanelli began his turn to speak, it felt like watching a predator waiting for the perfect moment to swoop down on unsuspecting prey.

After recapping the undisputed facts of the case, Fanelli said, it's unclear "whether her father even attempted suicide or [it] was an attempt to alleviate his pain. . . . But Mr. Forray says that there's some nefarious conduct here by Ms. Mancini because she called about the prescription of morphine."

At that point, Fanelli pounced. "As is abundantly laid out in medical records," he said, "Mr. Yourshaw had previously been prescribed morphine and it hadn't been delivered."[2]

Hearing this bombshell, Forray immediately leapt from his chair. "Mr. Fanelli is arguing matters that are not part of the record and not part of the testimony!"

Fanelli explained that this stunning information came from hospice records we obtained during discovery. It was appropriate for the court to consider those records, he told Judge Russell, because prosecution witnesses repeatedly referred to them at the preliminary hearing.

"Let me stop you there, Mr. Fanelli," Judge Russell said. "My decision has to be based upon what is [already] in evidence. I'm not going to be able to make a decision based upon additional information you're providing me that's not in this transcript."

Fanelli then asked that my father's hospice records be admitted into evidence, so the court could consider them. "I don't think there should be any objection to that, as those [records] were provided in discovery."

At this, Forray again vaulted out of his chair, and bellowed, "Your honor, I am not going to agree, and I object!"

---

1. Transcript of Petition for Habeas Corpus at 11-12, *Commw. of Pa. v. Mancini*, (2013) (No. CR1305-2013).

2. *Id.* at 13-14.

"You made an argument to me about Ms. Mancini seeking morphine," Judge Russell told Forray, "and my impression was that this man had not had morphine before. . . . I hope you are giving me an appropriate picture of what actually happened."

"I am, your Honor," Forray said, adding a profoundly important qualifier, "based on my knowledge of this matter and the testimony that was presented." He reiterated that we were offering new information that should not be allowed at this stage of the process.

Fanelli replied, "The records were not introduced at the preliminary hearing because we didn't have access to them. . . . I'm telling the Court that opioids were prescribed for Mr. Yourshaw in advance of this call by Ms. Mancini."[3]

At this point, my husband, Joe, noticed that Captain Durkin reached for a file in front of him at the prosecution's table, pulled it up against his chest, and began to quietly leaf through the pages.

Fanelli pressed his advantage. If he was wrong about what the newly revealed records say, he told Judge Russell, the prosecution should agree to let the court consider them, because it will help the prosecution's case. "But if I'm right," he said, "then the Court should have all of the information."

Forray, now appearing thoroughly vexed, complained that "essentially counsel is now asking for a second preliminary hearing. . . . His opportunity to question [Hospice of Central Pennsylvania team leader] Ms. Hornberger [about any opioid prescription] frankly was at the time of the preliminary hearing. . . . For whatever reason, they chose not to ask those questions."

At this point, I was practically shouting to myself, "The reason was that we couldn't ask about records that we didn't have and didn't get until after the hearing!"

"We're not trying to hide anything from the Court," Forray said, "but I don't think counsel should be able to go out and essentially try to put on new evidence at this point to attack a decision that was made by a District Justice literally two months ago."

3. *Id.* at 14-17.

Judge Russell said, "Well, Mr. Fanelli said he didn't have this information. The only one who had this information was the Commonwealth. It appears that this is something that counsel should be able to stipulate on or agree on."

Perhaps not realizing the gravity of what he was about to admit, Forray said, "Your Honor, as I stand here, I'm not aware of that information and again, based on the testimony of the hospice nurse, the team leader, she apparently was unaware of that information either. So I'm telling the Court I don't know that that information does or doesn't exist."[4]

Fanelli had a ready cure for Forray's ignorance, saying, "As an offer of proof, your Honor, I would ask if the Court would permit me to introduce a physician's plan of care to you with a stamp on it of January 18th from hospice, indicating that the idea for Mr. Yourshaw was morphine sulfate 20 milligrams/milliliters. And it says 'oral pain meds may be titrated 1 to 2 times the base dose' . . . So it's right in the record. I'm not making it up."

Ending with a not-so-subtle jab at his adversary, Fanelli said, "I don't doubt for one second Mr. Forray may not have read this, okay, but it's there."

Judge Russell asked Forray, "In all fairness . . . [should] he not be allowed to supplement the record with this information?"

Forray held the page with this damning information, looked it over, and stammered: "Well, your Honor, I'm looking at this paper. I don't recognize this piece of paper as in . . . it doesn't look like the rest of the hospice notes, but I don't . . . I'm not suggesting that this was in some fashion created or whatever. Again, your Honor, this was not the testimony at the preliminary hearing."

Judge Russell seemed perplexed that Forray was not familiar with this piece of evidence. "But did you supply these records to Mr. Fanelli?"

Forray said, "I don't recognize this particular document. . . . I don't have all the hospice notes with me, your Honor." As if to say he didn't do all his homework because there was too much of it, he told Judge Russell, "The rest of the file is extensive."

4. *Id.* at 20.

Forray groped for a way to explain the discrepancy between the written evidence and his witnesses' testimony. "If the document that Mr. Fanelli is referencing is a physician's plan of care," he said, "for whatever reason apparently that plan was never followed."[5]

Joe noticed that police Captain Durkin had pulled the document being discussed—the hospice physician's plan of care—from his file, slid it over to Forray, and tugged on Forray's sleeve. Forray pushed the page back to Durkin without even glancing at it.

It was now clear to all in the courtroom that Senior Deputy Attorney General Anthony Forray, a career prosecutor, had not even bothered to read the evidence he'd possessed from the beginning. Nor did Forray bother to verify the hospice witnesses' claims that the reason my father was on morphine was because I had insisted on it. This physician's plan of care, located just a few pages from the front of the hospice chart, put the lie to those statements.

Forray's argument—that I'd had a nefarious intent when I called about morphine for Dad—evaporated. Here was evidence that a physician wrote an order for morphine two weeks before I called—an order that had not been carried out.

But Forray was not ready to concede, so Fanelli asked Judge Russell to officially re-open the record, a procedural step that would allow her to legally consider the newly-revealed evidence.

"I feel that it's appropriate to allow you the opportunity to supplement the record," Judge Russell said. "But you tell me how you plan to do it, if the Commonwealth doesn't agree" that the information is valid. Fanelli said he would subpoena the custodian of records from the hospice or get an affidavit from the hospice that the records are accurate.

Returning to his main argument, Fanelli launched an eloquent attack on the core of the case against me: "We do know it's established law of the land that a terminally ill patient in hospice care, as Mr. Yourshaw was, has the constitutional right to take as much medicine as he needs to alleviate his pain even if it hastens his death."

5. *Id.* at 23.

The "right" in question here, Fanelli said, is "not the right of the state to dictate that someone has to suffer in pain and be kept alive in pain," but "the right of the person to self-determination. Should you be able to take as much medicine as you need to stop your pain even if it results in your death? The court has said yes—it is 'a fundamental right.'"[6]

At this point, everyone in the courtroom was spellbound.

Judge Russell turned to Forray and asked, "What is the evidence in the record that the gentleman had consumed the medication with the intent to commit suicide as opposed to the intent to relieve the pain he was in? . . . We have to know that you have proof of this man's intent."

Forray said, "I think his intentions were clear that he wanted to die, based on his statements to numerous people including the nurse." Speaking of the hospice nurse, he said, "She said that he made clear he wanted to die. That was his desire. He didn't want to get better."

"As do many, many, many people, elderly people or very sick people," Judge Russell replied. "They make those statements. Whether they actually want to die is another thing; . . . when they're obviously in pain, they say that. Whether they mean it or not is another thing."

Forray's assertion to Judge Russell that Dad "didn't want to get better," to me, was the most offensive part of the entire morning's argument. My father was suffering, physically and existentially. He was ninety-three years old, in pain, and he could no longer do the things that gave his life meaning. He was dying. I thought: "Please tell me, Mr. Forray, how do you 'get better' from dying?"

Rebutting Forray, Fanelli renewed his attack on the basic premise of the Commonwealth's case. "Whether he intended to kill himself, who knows at that precise time when he was drinking the medicine? Was he in intractable pain and just couldn't take anymore [*sic*]?"

Not only that, Fanelli said, the assisted suicide law was unconstitutionally vague. "I could dream up a bunch of scenarios" that might be covered. "Mr. Yourshaw is a diabetic, and his blood sugars are out of control. . . . He fed himself candy and soda because that's what he

6. *Id.* at 29.

wanted. Now we know that if you take candy and soda and you have uncontrolled diabetes, you can put yourself into a diabetic coma and die. But if you've got a 93-year-old man who is at the end of the road and he wants a Hershey bar and a can of soda, are you going to say to him 'You can't have it—it might make your diabetes worse'? But if you give him that can of soda, are you assisting in his attempted suicide, because he's somehow maybe trying to get himself into a diabetic coma and die?"

Wrapping up, Fanelli challenged the prosecution witnesses' claims that my father intended to commit suicide and that I intended to help him do so. "We need independent evidence of a crime," he said, "before you can rely on those statements."[7]

Forray was not about to give up. "Irrespective of the document that Mr. Fanelli wants to have introduced," he said, "fundamentally you have a man who was on no medications, he made it clear he didn't want to be on medication. You have the defendant's phone call on the 1st and her insistence that morphine be prescribed."

Judge Russell: "Is there evidence in your record that this man was in pain?"

Forray admitted, "He did say [to hospice workers] he was in pain."

"Because that would seem to be an odd medical situation where an elderly person that has a lot of problems and is in pain, but he's prescribed no pain medication," Judge Russell said.

"He didn't want to be on pain medication," Forray said. "He had stopped all his medication, and I think that's clearly established in the record."

Judge Russell, clearly doubtful, said, "Well, it will be interesting to read that because it seems odd that a person in pain would not want pain medicine."

"Right," Forray said. "But for whatever reason he didn't want any treatment in terms of any medication. And again, at the preliminary hearing the hospice supervisor basically said he had never been on opioids."[8]

---

7. *Id.* at 28-33.
8. *Id.* at 37-38.

Once again, Forray was regurgitating false information that would have been obvious if he'd done due diligence in checking his witnesses' claims. He didn't know that Dad's medical records showed that he had been on opioids before, a low dose that wasn't effective but left him with side effects that compounded his suffering. Forray didn't know that the medical records showed Dad was self-medicating for pain at home with a lot of Tylenol and ibuprofen.

Fanelli renewed his request to provide Judge Russell with the critical hospice and medical records. Forray, now realizing he'd been eclipsed, said, "Your Honor, the Commonwealth is not going to be difficult at this point. . . . I'm satisfied that that's a document that exists within the hospice notes. However, your Honor, I would indicate that if admitted, [the information in the records] is *completely inconsistent with the testimony that was presented.*"[9] (Emphasis added.)

BOOM! With that admission, the Commonwealth's case had just imploded. The prosecutor's fatal mistakes had been exposed in open court: He hadn't bothered to read the evidence he'd had in his possession from the beginning; he'd never verified his witnesses' statements against the information in the hospice and medical records—information that eviscerated the Commonwealth's case. Forray's attempts to counter or evade this damaging revelation failed. He looked like he'd been duped by his own witnesses because of his own incompetence. By contrast, Fanelli looked brilliant. I felt like I'd just been defended by Clarence Darrow himself.

As we filed out of the courtroom, Fanelli pulled me off into an alcove in the hallway. Smiling from ear to ear, he whispered, "How do you feel about how it went?"

"Pretty good, I think," I answered, as media photographers clicked away at our impromptu conference.

"It couldn't have gone any better for us in there today," he said, beaming, then strode confidently down the hallway to the exit.

---

9. *Id.* at 40-41.

CHAPTER 11

A Long Wait and a Difficult Aftermath

Oh, my friend,
it's not what they take away from you that counts.
It's what you do with what you have left.

—Hubert Humphrey

IF THE CASE against me had been a Broadway show, it was a bomb that would have closed after the prosecution's disastrous performance before Judge Russell—if not sooner. But the attorney general's office pressed on, and the case continued to draw withering criticism in the press.

Los Angeles Times columnist Steve Lopez wrote, "I keep waiting for the news that prosecutors in Pennsylvania have come to their senses and dropped criminal charges against Barbara Mancini. . . . Having watched my own father wither away in his last days of hospice care, I can say with certainty that if he'd asked for morphine, I'd have given him as much as he wanted. The idea that such an act of love and compassion can be considered a crime is beyond my comprehension."[1]

In the blog *Litigation & Trial*, Pennsylvania lawyer Max Kennerly wrote, "Our Commonwealth has the absurd notion that what allegedly happened to Mr. Yourshaw was a terrible crime." Noting that my father "died exactly how he didn't want to die, at a hospital after suffering

1. http://articles.latimes.com/2013/nov/05/local/la-me-1106-lopez-dyingwell-20131106.

through days of pain and extraordinary measures," Kennerly lamented the power of prosecutors to pursue such a flawed case. "State prosecutors exist in a world unto themselves," he wrote. Even though most are elected, they are "practically accountable to no one."[2]

Fred Fanelli expected Judge Russell to issue her ruling in about two months, and he was quite optimistic she would rule in my favor. Back home in Philadelphia, I allowed myself to feel some glimmers of hope. My outlook was helped by messages of support from people like Russell Smith, a physician whom I knew from my days as a student nurse. "This prosecution is wrong in so many ways that I hardly know where to begin," Smith wrote. "I think your father was very fortunate to have had such a loving and competent caregiver as you." Referring to the chain of "callous actions" by the hospice, police, coroner, and prosecution, he wrote, "It's tragic that these people have turned what could have been a peaceful, dignified death into a nightmare, both for you and for your father in his last days."[3]

But waiting two months for the judge's ruling seemed like an eternity. After just three weeks, I started checking the Pennsylvania court system's web site every day. Every day, I saw the same bleak result on my computer screen: *Case Status–Active*, meaning that the judge had not dismissed the case. I'd scroll through the many pages of the docket, where every action in the case was listed, just to make sure the judge hadn't shocked us all and handed down a ruling against me.

As the time without a resolution dragged on, my father's final days played on an endless loop in my mind. If I somehow managed to block out those thoughts, my mind would fill the void with unstoppable agitation about the injustice inflicted on me. I'd replay the outrages perpetrated by the hospice, by the police, by the district magistrate, by the coroner, by the attorney general's office. To say nothing of the financial strain: We had enough to pay our bills, but we had to borrow the money for legal fees. Without question, the financial hit was huge. I tried and failed to divert my thoughts to other things. Activities that I

2. http://www.litigationandtrial.com/2013/10/articles/attorney/civil-rights-1/barbara-mancini/.
3. Personal communication, September 9, 2013.

once enjoyed—theater, concerts, music—offered no relief. Nearly every waking moment, and much of the time I was asleep, I was tormented.

Continuing my long daily F-bomb therapy walks in the Wissahickon Valley with our dog, Dano, was the only thing that helped. In those quiet woods, I could calm myself enough to reflect on how I'd become trapped in this nightmare. I tried to put myself in nurse Cattermole's shoes and imagine what she had been thinking that day. Did she really feel a terrible crime had occurred? Was she truly scared? She knew Dad had been prescribed morphine when he re-entered hospice care—why did she or her hospice co-workers fail to mention that to police and prosecutors? Why would she falsely testify that I asked for more morphine because Dad "had not died yet"? Was their goal to divert scrutiny from their failures as hospice care providers? Perhaps once she, Ms. Woods, and Ms. Hornberger started down the path of telling falsehoods, they were unable to extricate themselves, and they continued them to paint me in the worst possible light.

But mostly, I continued to burn with anger. The sloppy way the prosecution handled the case made me realize how unimportant I was to those who now possessed tremendous power over my life, my livelihood, and my freedom. I was nothing more than a docket number, an inconsequential spoke in the massive wheel of criminal justice, a mere notch in the belt of a prosecutor eager to boast about a long record of convictions.

Tom Petty became my steady music companion. From the early days of my ordeal, his song "I Won't Back Down" had been high on my playlist. The song describes a person facing terrible circumstances but who is determined to fight back, even though it will be a bruising and difficult journey. I would also listen over and over to his ballad "The Waiting," whose refrain describes how hard it is to wait for an outcome while your entire life is on hold.

Six weeks after my habeas corpus hearing I received a phone call from a nurse, Christine, whom I had worked with in the ER. "How are you holding up?" she asked. "We're all thinking about you at work and wishing for the best." We talked briefly and then her voice cracked, and she began to sob. "I feel so terrible about what's happened to you. You are the person that everyone admires. I can't imagine how you're going through this, but I am so proud to know you." She was so distraught during the call that she made to support me that I ended up consoling *her*. I had no idea that I was so admired, and that my ordeal was having such an impact on my co-workers. And I admit that I felt deeply touched by her raw expression of distress over what was happening to me. My family and I were not the only ones suffering through this.

Originally, Fanelli thought for sure that Judge Russell would rule by Thanksgiving. But Thanksgiving came, and the list of things we could be thankful for did not include the end of my case. Trying to reassure me, Fanelli said, "I'm expecting a decision in the next couple of weeks. I'm very confident." But I checked the computerized court docket daily, to no avail.

As Christmas approached, Judge Russell ordered attorneys on both sides of the case to submit final briefs by December 27. There would be no Christmas gift for me from Judge Russell.

Three months after the hearing, into mid-January, we were still waiting. Fanelli continued to have confidence the ruling would be in my favor, but he was at a loss to explain why it was taking so long. The uncertainty of life in limbo, with my entire future on hold, was excruciating. Being unable to speak about it compounded my frustration.

I told Fanelli I had reached my limit; I simply had to get my side of the story out. I had learned so much about how the hospice had mistreated my father, how police and prosecutors can railroad an innocent person, how the criminal justice system fails to deliver justice. I wanted the world to know.

He quickly squashed that idea. "Barbara, if you violate the gag order, you will be arrested and probably spend at least a weekend in jail. Then you will end up in front of a different judge with a whole new problem on top of what you already have. Don't do it," he said. "You have to be patient." I resigned myself to the misery of waiting, waiting, waiting for the judge's decision.

The long, dark nights of January slowly gave way to winter's shortest and most bitter month. I checked, and checked, and checked the case status—no change. Friday, February 7, marked the one-year anniversary of my arrest. I checked again, and my search told me, as it always did: "Case Status – Active." No decision yet. Monday, February 10, I checked again. No change.

The next day was the one-year anniversary of Dad's death. We planned no special remembrance; we were living with the pain and fallout from it every day. I spoke with Mom early in the day as I always do, then took a longer than usual walk in the biting winter air, tramping through a light dusting of snow. Returning to the house in mid-afternoon, I sat down at the computer with some hot tea and once again entered my information into the Pennsylvania Court system case search field.

Finally, I found the words I'd spent so many weeks looking for:

"Case status—Closed . . . Charge Dismissed."

I whooped and hollered and grabbed my daughter and held her in a tight hug. We both started sobbing and cheering at the same time, ecstatic as relief washed over us and the burden of the last year burst away. We made so much noise that we woke Joe, who had been sleeping after working a night shift. He groggily stumbled down the stairs, concerned that something terrible had happened. I was so overcome I couldn't answer him. I just handed my computer over so he could read the news himself. Finally, we were free.

The next few days were a whirlwind of media coverage, interviews, and celebrations. I fielded call after call of congratulations, as did Mom and the rest of my family. The hospital where I worked immediately offered my job back, but I deferred, knowing I needed some time to decompress. Producers at the CBS television news magazine *60 Minutes* arranged a preliminary interview. I was energized, exhilarated, and exhausted all at once. I had my life back!

When Fanelli forwarded Judge Russell's forty-six-page decision to me, he gloated, "Jackie Russell beat the shit out of them with that ruling." He wasn't exaggerating. She ripped the case apart, piece by piece.

"An accused cannot be found to have aided, and then caused a third person to attempt suicide, without competent proof that an attempted suicide had indeed occurred,"[4] she wrote. On that point, "The Commonwealth clearly failed to present sufficient evidence."[5]

Testimony from the witnesses, the judge wrote, was unpersuasive and unreliable. "Some of the recollected thoughts expressed by the witnesses were contradicted or rendered vague or confusing by later testimony offered by those same witnesses."[6] Judge Russell also faulted the prosecution for "relying upon statements she [Barbara Mancini] allegedly had made to witnesses—some of which were clarified or significantly modified between direct and cross-examination."[7] (Which is how a judge says, "Your cross-examination was devastating, Mr. Fanelli.")

The case was so bad, the prosecution didn't even explain the significance of the physical evidence it presented. "Although the precise morphine levels found in his blood were recited via stipulation into the record, no explanation was offered as to their meaning and significance,"[8] the ruling said. "The Commonwealth did not offer competent evidence indicating that Mr. Yourshaw actually died from 'morphine toxicity' or if his death was related in any manner to the morphine he had ingested at home or medication [morphine] that he had received while hospitalized."[9]

On and on Judge Russell went. "No one testified that he or she had heard [my father] express any intent to kill himself by taking morphine or doing some other self-destructive act at any time. The elderly man's alleged statements that he desired to die are not equivalent to expressions of an intent to kill himself."[10] Furthermore, the ruling said that if the hospice knew my father "wanted to die" and could take a potentially fatal amount of morphine on his own, "it was left unexplained . . . why the morphine, nevertheless, was allowed to remain within Mr. Yourshaw's control."[11]

4. *Commw. of Pa. v. Mancini,* No. 1305-13, C.P. Schuylkill Ct., Feb. 11, 2014, p. 45.
5. *Id.* at 34.
6. *Id.* at 34,35.
7. *Id.* at 40.
8. *Id.* at 36.
9. *Id.* at 24.
10. *Id.* at 37.
11. *Id.* at 38.

My decision not to call 911 was not part of a criminal act, the judge wrote. "His daughter knew, as did Hospice [*sic*] personnel, that it would be contrary to Mr. Yourshaw's wishes if he were taken to the hospital when in the final moments of his life."[12]

As for the claim that my calling to get morphine for my father was supposedly part of a criminal act? It was the heart of the case against me, and Judge Russell drove a stake right through it. "The Commonwealth's own witness conceded, however, that Mr. Yourshaw's physician prescribed the pain medication, with the apparent belief that it was proper to do so to address the elderly man's pain."[13]

It's a good thing for Senior Deputy Attorney General Forray that this case wasn't a moot court proceeding in law school, because Judge Russell would have flunked him. "The Commonwealth may not rely on suspicion and conjecture to prove its case,"[14] she wrote. "The Commonwealth's case appears to have been based on little independent investigation, significant hearsay—including double hearsay, received from third persons—speculation, [and] guess."[15]

Judge Russell's ruling ends with the most welcome words I've ever read: "The charge lodged against the Defendant is DISMISSED and Defendant is DISCHARGED.[16]" I wondered if she purposely held off issuing her ruling until the anniversary of my father's death, as a way of bringing some joy to that very sad date.

While I was jubilant over the dismissal, and Fanelli was too, he had to warn me that I was not yet out of limbo. Attorney General Kathleen Kane could appeal Judge Russell's ruling. She had thirty days to decide.

If she did appeal, it was not going to be a popular decision. Judge Russell's ruling prompted editorials and commentaries castigating Kane's handling of the case. From Pottsville, scene of the alleged "crime," the

12. *Id.* at 39-40.
13. *Id.* at 41.
14. *Id.* at 27.
15. *Id.* at 40.
16. *Id.*

Republican-Herald newspaper's editorial said, "The judge appears to have committed a mercy killing of a bad case. Kane should let it go."[17] The Harrisburg *Patriot News* agreed. "Barbara Mancini is no criminal. . . . It was a miscarriage of justice from the day charges were filed. Trying to revive the case against Mancini, and send her to prison for doing what her dying father wanted, would be the height of arrogance."[18] An editorial in the (Central PA) *Sentinel* suggested that the ruling delivered Attorney General Kane "judicial chastisement for prosecutorial ineptness" and urged her to forgo any appeal.[19] One of my most staunch defenders, columnist Paul Carpenter with the *Allentown Morning Call*, blasted Kane's case as "not just weak" but "nonexistent," and "an outrage." Carpenter wrote that the court delivered a "scathing" ruling, one that left "the impression that Kane has all the compassion and grace of Attila the Hun."[20]

Thirteen days after the ruling, on February 24, 2014, Kane's office announced her decision. Rather than speaking to the press, and facing potentially uncomfortable questions, she put out a written statement saying, "After careful consideration, Office of the Attorney General will not appeal the Decision." Admitting the obvious, the statement said, "An appeal would not have a substantial likelihood of success."

Kane should have had stopped there, but she couldn't resist sounding like a sore loser. The problem, she suggested, was not her judgment in pursuing a fatally flawed case based on no reliable evidence. In her view, the problem was simply that people were unhappy with her for enforcing a law that proved unpopular in this particular case.

"If the citizens of the Commonwealth disagree with an existing statute," Kane's statement said, "it is incumbent upon the people to work with the General Assembly to amend the law. Until such amendment occurs, it is the legal responsibility of prosecutors to enforce the law as it currently exists."[21]

---

17. Editorial, *The Republican Herald*, February 13, 2014.
18. http://www.pennlive.com/opinion/index.ssf/2014/02/barbara_mancini_joseph_yoursha.html.
19. Editorial, *The Sentinel*, February 15, 2014.
20. . http://articles.mcall.com/2014-02-18/news/mc-pc-kathleen-kane-credibility-20140218_1_kathleen-kane-barbara-mancini-joseph-yourshaw.
21. http://www.pottsmerc.com/general-news/20140225/pa-ag-will-drop-daughters-assisted-suicide-case.

Columnist Paul Carpenter delivered an acerbic retort. "So, it is the people of Pennsylvania, *except* for the attorney general, who are to blame for Mancini's difficulties," he wrote. "Prosecuting somebody for a crime without evidence is not the problem."

Pennsylvania law needs to be changed, all right, Carpenter wrote. "The Mancini case illustrates what can happen with laws that let prosecutors go after people for things that should be none of the government's business."[22]

My allies at Compassion and Choices cheered Kane's decision to forgo an appeal. "Barbara Mancini's prosecution was an abuse of power, an invasion of Joe Yourshaw's right to a peaceful death and a waste of taxpayer money," president Barbara Coombs Lee said. Fred Fanelli made a point that I would eventually start sharing with audiences around the country. The case, he told the media, "certainly raised some issues about what family members are faced with when they are caring for a loved one in the end stages of life. It's a scary prospect to know that the decisions you make can be judged critically in the lens of a prosecutor."[23]

Two weeks after the case was dismissed, Joe and I zipped up to New York on Amtrak's Acela express train to be interviewed by Anderson Cooper for *60 Minutes*. At the train station, CBS had a car waiting to pick us up. Instead of going to the CBS studio, we were taken to the Waldorf Astoria hotel, where a luxurious suite had been turned into a temporary TV set. Demand for the network studio was so intense, producer Andy Court explained, that they almost never got to use it. He mentioned that this was the same suite the Saudi royal family would use on visits to New York—and it definitely looked royal-worthy. The huge sitting room had a high ceiling trimmed with gold cornice, lush draperies on the windows, and gold accents on the walls, along with floral-accented carpet. There was an elegant large dining area, complete with a massive oak table, and

22. http://articles.mcall.com/2014-02-27/news/mc-pc-kathleen-kane-assisted-suicide-20140227_1_barbara-mancini-joseph-yourshaw-kathleen-kane.

23. http://articles.mcall.com/2014-02-24/news/mc-schuylkill-barbara-mancini-suicide-charge-20140224_1_barbara-mancini-joe-yourshaw-aiding-suicide.

there was marble everywhere, even in the bathroom. In the sitting area, cameras, lighting equipment, monitors, screens, and sophisticated audio equipment filled the entire space, with thick black cables snaking around the floor.

Off-air, chatting before the cameras came on, Anderson Cooper was very personable. During the interview, though, he was the hard-charging journalist, asking tough questions. I didn't mind. From my dealings with lawyers, I was used to pointed questioning. Cooper was just doing his job. Like a lawyer, he would ask the same question different ways. It wasn't hostile, but it felt like he was trying to get me to admit that I did indeed plan to help my father end his life.

When the interview ended after two-and-a-half hours, Andy Court was thrilled. "We don't have to tape anything over," he told me. "That's the first time that's happened!" And Anderson Cooper turned back into a caring human being, talking with me about his mom and discussions they'd had about end-of-life planning. Several of the crew mentioned to me how sorry they were about what happened to my dad and me—an encouraging sign that things had gone well. On the train ride home, Joe and I were so emotionally drained that we hardly said a word to each other.

Fanelli had urged me to return to work as quickly as possible, but now doubts were beginning to creep in. Would I be able to put this behind me and function as a nurse again? I arranged to stop in at the ER to speak with my manager and say hi to my co-workers. Everyone received me with great warmth and empathy, but I only lasted a few minutes before I burst into tears. This was going to be much harder than I anticipated. Even though my ordeal had "officially" ended, in the deep recesses of my psyche, it was not over yet.

Yes, in the end, justice had triumphed—I was exonerated. I was free! I had spent the past year waiting for this to happen. But why, just two weeks after a very happy ending to my nightmare, did I feel so awful? I felt depressed, a despair as deep as what I felt after being arrested. I never saw this coming. I kept asking myself: "What is wrong with me?" Every time I saw a police car, it struck fear into my heart—I worried I would be stopped and be arrested on some minor pretense. I was free, but I was paralyzed.

It was time for professional help—an experience that took an odd turn.

The therapist had her office in Philadelphia's historic Chestnut Hill neighborhood, on a quiet, narrow side street, in an old stone building with a wooden gate. She was a forty-something woman, petite, kindly, with shoulder-length blondish hair. I settled into an armchair amid potted plants and comfortable furniture, and, with a white noise machine running to make sure no one outside the door could hear, I launched into some cognitive behavioral therapy. The idea is that talking to the therapist can help change the way you think, which in turn enables you to make positive changes in your behavior.

After hearing my story, the therapist concluded that I suffered from post-traumatic stress disorder. Over the next six weeks or so, she gave me good advice on coping strategies. But as we wrapped up that first phase, she made a stunning offer: She could connect me with a medium who could let me talk to my dead father.

Whoa, I thought, that's too far out there for me. I figured I was almost ready to walk in the door at work and be a nurse again, so I decided I'd carry on without her help. Going into counseling, I'd had no illusions that I would get over the entire traumatic experience quickly, and I hadn't. I just wanted to be able to get back to work without falling apart.

On April 23, *60 Minutes* sent a camera crew to Pottsville to shoot background footage for the episode about my case. At the end of the day, cameraman Don Lee told me something I will never forget. "I've been all over the world," he said. "I've seen some terrible things. And I have to tell you that I am horrified about what happened to you."

The next week I felt ready to return to work in the ER. Despite my apprehension, it was good to be back at work. In many ways, it felt like I had never left, and I was able to be the ER nurse I knew how to be. My colleagues warmly welcomed me back. I'd never been hugged so many times in my life.

To an outside observer, it appeared I had returned to normal life. We attended gatherings with family and friends where my case finally was no longer the topic of conversation. I took a few day trips. We planted our vegetable and flower gardens. Dano and I still took our daily walks. We chatted with the neighbors. Yet I was deeply wounded by my experience. I had yet to mourn my father's death; my grief lay dormant in a corner of my soul, unexplored, untouched, and overwhelmed by trying to survive a yearlong assault. I wasn't sure if it was possible to be the person I once was and resume my previous life. I couldn't help thinking about all the people who might find themselves in the same wrenching, life-altering predicament, simply for giving compassionate care to their dying loved ones. I felt like I had unfinished business.

Although I could not undo my father's terrible death, I decided that I could speak out and expose what happened to us. I learned how powerful my story could be the first time I ever gave a public talk about what my father and I went through.

About forty people—a salt-and-pepper mix of gray-haired seniors with a sprinkling of millennials—had come to an event organized by Compassion and Choices. The topic: Issues and Options at the End of Life. The setting: a community room in a Center City Philadelphia condo complex. The speakers: a state senator, a neurologist, a pharmacist, and me.

Going in, I'd been nervous. I had never done public speaking before. But I'd prepared carefully, giving a lot of thought about the best way to use my twenty minutes. I told the audience about how things can go wrong—horribly wrong—at the end of life, even when someone had carefully planned ahead, as my father had done.

Not long after I started to speak, the room grew silent except for my voice. Simply hearing the facts of what happened to me and my father was riveting. Afterward, I was besieged by people who had lined up to talk to me. Many said they had followed my case from the beginning. Some expressed fears for themselves and their loved ones; others spoke of their own painful experiences. I talked to well-wishers until it was past time to leave the room and we had to be shooed out.

It was clear: People wanted to hear what I had to say. Unlike so many who have been victimized by powerful forces beyond their control, I had a voice that would be heard. I wanted to use it. From there, I decided I would welcome any chance to speak for improved end-of-life care, even as I continued to work part-time in the emergency room. More invitations to speak followed, and I got the same reaction, so I knew I was on the right path.

---

60 Minutes aired my story in the episode "Ending Life" on Sunday, October 19, 2014. After my tough interview with Anderson Cooper back in February 2014, I wasn't sure how *60 Minutes* would portray me and my case. But I was hopeful. When producer Andy Court called to say the show would air soon, he said they had consulted a hospice expert who was appalled at the way my father was treated.

At the time, an impassioned debate on end-of-life issues was underway in the country, thanks to Brittany Maynard, a twenty-nine-year-old newlywed who had been diagnosed with a fatal brain cancer. She and her family moved to Oregon to establish residency so she could use that state's medical aid-in-dying law. *People* magazine had featured her story, and she had made a compelling video about her decision to die at age twenty-nine. An articulate and self-determined young woman, Brittany told the world that she believed that everyone with a terminal illness deserved the option that she would use there in Oregon. Capitalizing on the attention Brittany Maynard had drawn, the *60 Minutes* episode featured her and explored the questions her case raised about the ethics of hastening someone's death.

In the parts about my case, the episode did a good job exposing how the medical and legal systems forced my father to suffer the painful hospital death he'd carefully planned to avoid, and how I was persecuted for trying to honor his wishes. It ended on a poignant note:

> BARBARA MANCINI: *There are some nights I lie awake in bed and I just relive this whole thing. And less of it has to do with what happened to me. More of it has to do with picturing him lying there in that ER crying out, knowing what I read in the hospital record.*
> ANDERSON COOPER: *The way he died haunts you?*
> BARBARA MANCINI: *Yes. Because the way his life ended was exactly the way he didn't want it to end. With no control, in pain, having things done to him. And I feel terrible about it.*

The following day, there was a health fair in Pottsville, the town where my father lived and died. The Hospice of Central Pennsylvania had originally agreed to sponsor a booth at the fair, but now it decided not to show up. Instead of displaying the HCP logo, the empty booth carried a small, a hand-written sign for a travel agent.

The *60 Minutes* story produced a surge in donations to my legal defense fund, and I was able to recover much more of my expenses. I will always be grateful to the many people who offered support to me and my family. It renewed my faith in humanity and affirmed that I was doing the right thing in speaking out.

Prompted, no doubt, by the *60 Minutes* piece, I began to receive more and more speaking requests. I found it increasingly difficult to manage the necessary time off and travel with my emergency room job. So, in November, after eight months back at work, I left my nursing career behind and signed a contract with Compassion and Choices as a speaker and consultant. In my new career, I would be confronting our society's taboos surrounding death, and challenging powerful forces—in religion, health care, the law and politics—that limit our control over how we die.

CHAPTER 12

We Die Differently Now

Death, in most cases, is no longer a sudden conflagration, but a long, drawn-out slow burn.

—Haider Warraich, MD

I OFTEN OPEN talks about my experience by telling an obvious truth that usually jolts the audience to attention and prompts a few nervous laughs. I warn them, "You are going to die. The people you love and care about will die. The only question is how and when." I tell them that the same wonderful changes that enable us to live longer—modern sanitation, revolutionary advances in medical treatment, and better personal health habits—have also changed the way we die.

If you were alive in 1900, you were most likely to die of infectious diseases, such as pneumonia, influenza, tuberculosis, and gastrointestinal infections. If you escaped those plagues and lived long enough, you might then die of heart disease, stroke, or kidney disease. Cancer barely made the top ten causes of death.[1] When any of those diseases hit, there was little that doctors could do for a patient. The average life expectancy was only 47.3 years of age.[2]

One hundred years later, the typical American could expect to live 78.7 years, a gain of more than 30 years. Public sanitation, antibiotics,

1. http://demography.cpc.unc.edu/2014/06/16/mortality-and-cause-of-death-1900-v-2010/.
2. http://demography.cpc.unc.edu/2014/06/16/mortality-and-cause-of-death-1900-v-2010/.

and immunizations helped vanquish many infectious diseases. By the year 2000, the leading killers were conditions that frequently produce long, drawn-out deaths that come after intensive, often painful, and definitely costly medical treatment. As physician and author Atul Gawande has noted, "These days, swift catastrophic illness is the exception. For most people, death comes only after a long medical struggle with an ultimately unstoppable condition. . . . In all cases, death is certain, but the timing isn't. . . . Technology can sustain our organs until we are well past the point of awareness and coherence."[3]

Seven of the top ten causes of death today[4]—heart disease, cancer, stroke, chronic lung disease, diabetes, Alzheimer's disease, and kidney disease—are from the kinds of chronic conditions that Gawande describes. Only three of the top ten—accidents, influenza, and sepsis—generally bring relatively quick deaths. Even then, that quick death often comes after heroic emergency measures are tried, and the patient will typically die in a hospital, attended by doctors and nurses, rather than with loved ones.

As modern medicine helps people with chronic diseases live longer, their health often steadily declines, and their physical discomfort gets progressively worse. My mother-in-law, for example, had high blood pressure for years, then suffered for over a decade with chronic kidney disease. She spent eleven years on kidney dialysis, getting treatments three times a week. Her skin was punctured with large needles connecting her to machines that would cleanse her blood of toxins during a session lasting over four hours each time. Dialysis kept her alive but left her feeling completely spent and exhausted. She endured bone fractures, a heart attack, and eventually a toe infection that developed into gangrene of her foot. After her leg was amputated below the knee, her vital organs soon shut down. Once every possible treatment had been tried, she spent one day in hospice care and died.

Another grim way many of us will die is the end-stage of heart failure. When your heart can no longer pump blood effectively to your lungs and other organs, it will leave you constantly short of breath, even when just

3. Atul Gawande. *Being Mortal*, Metropolitan Books, 2014, 156-157.
4. https://www.ncbi.nlm.nih.gov/pubmed/17408087.

sitting in a chair. Your legs and even your abdomen will swell with extra fluid, and despite ever-present fatigue, sleep will be elusive and fleeting because you have so much trouble breathing. And when your time finally comes, if you have an implantable defibrillator, your dying heart will get powerful electric jolts, so your last moments feel like a horse is kicking you in the chest.

Cancer deaths can be particularly painful, especially when cancer erupts where there is no room for the growing tumors, like the brain or the bones. And the toxic effects of cancer treatments are legion because the goal of chemotherapy and radiation is to kill the cancer cells without killing you. You can barely manage to eat anything, because the treatment leaves your stomach feeling like you are in a boat navigating nonstop twenty-foot waves.

Chronic lung disease, also known as COPD, (Chronic Obstructive Pulmonary Disease), is another gruesome way many of us will die. It kills by slowly suffocating you. You live tethered to an oxygen tank for years, but eventually the oxygen no longer helps, as your diseased lungs lose their ability to exchange air. Mucus clogs your air passages and violent coughing spasms wrack your frail and weakened body. The simple act of brushing your teeth may take all the energy you can muster before you collapse back in your chair in exhaustion. If you are placed on a ventilator to assist your breathing, you will never come off it. You will need a hole cut into your neck (a tracheostomy) after just a few days to make the connection permanent.

If you are unlucky enough to suffer irreversible brain damage, modern medicine can keep you alive, sometimes for decades. A ventilator will keep pumping air into your lungs, and surgical tubes placed in your stomach will keep you fed and hydrated indefinitely. That's what happened to Karen Ann Quinlan of Morris County, New Jersey, who collapsed in 1976 at the age of twenty-one, after drinking alcohol and taking sedative pills. Left unconscious, with permanent brain damage, she faced a life in a hospital bed, hooked up to machines that fed and breathed for her. Her parents believed she would not want to continue living that way, and they fought in court for the right to tell doctors to disconnect her ventilator. A year later, in a landmark ruling, the New Jersey Supreme Court unanimously agreed with her parents. Unexpectedly, Quinlan breathed on her own, and continued living in that vegetative state for another nine years before dying from other natural causes.[5]

A famous case involving Nancy Cruzan of Mt. Vernon, Missouri, raised similar legal and ethical issues. In 1983, at age twenty-five, she sustained severe brain trauma from a car crash and remained in a persistent vegetative state. As with Karen Ann Quinlan, her parents believed she would not choose to live such a life and would refuse life-extending treatment. It took them seven-and-a-half years, while they appealed her case through Missouri appellate courts, the US Supreme Court, and back to Missouri courts again, to get the right to end heroic medical treatment for their daughter. Cruzan died twelve days later.[6]

The power of modern medicine to keep a profoundly brain-injured person alive indefinitely provoked another famously controversial case in Florida in the early 2000s. Terry Schiavo's heart stopped in 1990 from a severe electrolyte imbalance, leaving her in what doctors agreed was a persistent vegetative state. Her husband was certain that Schiavo would have wanted to stop medical treatment and be allowed to die, but his legal efforts to that end were bitterly opposed by her parents and siblings and a legion of conservative religious supporters. The case drew international attention and prompted battles in Florida state courts, the Florida legislature, the US Congress, and federal courts before her husband finally won the undisputed right to discontinue Schiavo's feeding tube. She died two weeks later, in 2005.[7]

Those well-known legal battles failed to put an end to disputes surrounding a patient's choices at the end of life. At my speaking events, I've heard again and again about more recent cases where families struggle to honor a loved one's end-of-life wishes. Often, the resistance comes from health professionals who have different moral or religious values from the

5. http://www.nytimes.com/1985/06/12/nyregion/karen-ann-quinlan-31-dies-focus-of-76-right-to-die-case.html?pagewanted=all.

6. http://www.nytimes.com/1990/12/27/us/nancy-cruzan-dies-outlived-by-a-debate-over-the-right-to-die.html.

7. http://www.nytimes.com/2005/04/01/us/schiavo-dies-ending-bitter-case-over-feeding-tube.html?_r=0.

patient. A steady stream of ethical dilemmas plays out daily in hospitals and nursing homes because we have succeeded in staving off death, but our social attitudes and laws have not caught up with the sometimes-brutal power of modern medicine to prolong life at all costs.

For most of human history, death was not a medical event. Before the twentieth century, clergy dominated at the deathbed, where they ministered to the dying person's body and soul.[8] After the devastation of the bubonic plague in the fourteenth century, which killed twenty-five million people in Europe alone, Latin scholars penned the *Ars Moriendi*, manuals that instructed Catholic clergy and laypeople how to attain a "good death." Also used by Protestants, the manual prescribed prayers and rituals focusing on faith, humility, forgiveness, and redemption of sins.[9] In Judeo-Christian doctrine, pain and suffering were considered a part of dying well, as it allowed for spiritual atonement.

Advances in medicine and biology helped put physicians at odds with clergy at the bedside of the dying. Injectable morphine became commercially available by the mid-1800s. It was widely used in the US Civil War to treat wounded and dying soldiers.[10] Civilian physicians used it on patients undergoing surgery or childbirth and on those facing imminent death. Though clergy still ministered to a dying person's soul, the medical practitioner came to view pain and suffering not as sources of spiritual meaning, but as undesirable conditions that could be treated. It was accepted practice for physicians to use morphine, not only to treat a dying patient's pain, but also for "terminal sedation"—deliberately keeping a dying person asleep or unconscious until death occurs.

Terminal sedation was socially acceptable, because it fit with the religious doctrine of double effect. An idea dating back to the time of Thomas Aquinas in the eleventh century, the doctrine applies to an action that is known to cause two outcomes—one that is morally troubling; another

8. http://anesthesiology.pubs.asahq.org/article.aspx?articleid=1955413.
9. http://www.thehastingscenter.org/uploadedFiles/Publications/the-art-of-dying-well.pdf.
10. http://www.news-medical.net/health/Morphine-History.aspx.

that is morally good. As long as the intent is to produce the outcome that is morally good, the action is justified. In this case, a physician can give a dying patient enough medicine (usually morphine) to ease pain and suffering, even if it is known that it will cause death, as long as the *intent* is to relieve suffering.[11] Applying the doctrine of double effect to end-of-life cases is not without controversy; critics contend that proper doses of pain-killing medicine can deliver the desired relief without hastening death.[12]

Today in the United States, a dying person who is in considerable pain may choose to be sedated into unconsciousness, and then have food and fluids withheld until death occurs. Some deeply religious people believe that this amounts to killing the patient.[13] However, the US Supreme Court affirmed that dying patients have a constitutional right to make this choice.[14]

Some terminally ill patients who are not yet on their deathbed, such as those suffering from ALS or inoperable cancer, are nonetheless interested in deliberately acting to cause their own deaths—the literal definition of suicide. In most Judeo-Christian religions, suicide was, and still is, seen as self-murder, a sinful violation of the laws of God and the natural law of self-preservation.[15] However, some Eastern religions and cultures have more accepting attitudes. Hinduism and Buddhism both embrace the concept of reincarnation, raising the possibility that when you die you will be reborn into another, perhaps better, life.[16] The ancient Hindu Veda books allowed suicide for religious reasons. There was a long Hindu tradition, now rare, whereby widows would throw themselves onto their husbands' bodies on a funeral pyre to obtains blessings for them both. Stories of sacrificing one's own body for personal liberation can be found in ancient Buddhist texts, although Buddhism largely rejects suicide.[17] Imperial China sanctioned suicide by military generals who were defeated in battle, and suicide was considered an acceptable way

11. Giza Lopes. *Dying with Dignity: A Legal Approach to Assisted Death*. Praeger, 2015, 26-27.
12. https://plato.stanford.edu/entries/double-effect/.
13. https://www.orthocuban.com/2009/12/palliative-sedation-of-terminal-patients/.
14. https://www.law.cornell.edu/supct/html/95-1858.ZC.html.
15. http://www.pewforum.org/2013/11/21/religious-groups-views-on-end-of-life-issues/.
16. https://www.britannica.com/topic/reincarnation.
17. http://www.med.uio.no/klinmed/english/research/centres/nssf/articles/culture/Retterstol3.pdf.

to avoid public dishonor for people accused of crimes. Samurai warriors in Japan followed an honor code that included *seppuku*, the ritual by which a warrior would take his own life by using a sword to disembowel himself. Largely, attitudes toward suicide in Asian cultures are changing, and it is now generally viewed as a mental health crisis.[18]

No such acceptance of suicide occurred in Christianity. In mid-thirteenth century England, self-murder became a crime. English common law considered it a double offense: Not only was it a crime against the Almighty, it also was a crime against the English King because it deprived him of one of his subjects. The punishment for a successful suicide was the denial of a Christian burial. The body, instead, would be dumped on a crossroads with a wooden stake driven through it. The deceased's survivors were punished, too, by having their property seized by the Crown, leaving them impoverished. People who attempted suicide and were unsuccessful were jailed.[19] This practice persisted in England until the early nineteenth century, and it took another 150 years until suicide there was decriminalized. Massachusetts was the sole American colony that adopted the harsh English common law. Until 1823, a Massachusetts suicide victim's property was seized and the body impaled on a common highway.[20]

By the late 1800s most people recognized that "melancholia"—depression—was a driving force in taking one's own life. It came to be understood as an irrational act—something that would not be deterred by legal penalties. Even so, the law in most states still treated attempted suicide as a crime well into the latter half of the twentieth century. Suicide is no longer against the law anywhere in the United States, nor in most twenty-first-century societies. However, aiding or assisting suicide is still a crime in most Western countries.[21]

---

18. https://www.psychologytoday.com/blog/minority-report/201406/asian-honor-and-suicide.
19. http://www.bbc.com/news/magazine-14374296.
20. http://digitalcommons.law.villanova.edu/cgi/viewcontent.cgi?article=1823&context=vlr, p.3.
21. My personal opinion is that suicide is the premature ending of a person's life because of depression or despondency—a mental health crisis. There is a big distinction between that and the wish of the *dying* to have some control and say over how their lives will end. Most mental health professionals make this distinction, too, as does the American Association of Suicidology, which works to prevent suicides. I talk about this in speaking events in the context of the criminal statutes: Where aid-in-dying is allowed, the law does not consider it suicide. However, where aid-in-dying is illegal, it is considered assisted suicide or even manslaughter.

This raises the question: Should those statutes outlawing "assisting suicide" be applied even when terminally ill people who face great suffering want to expedite their inevitable deaths?

Many people disagree about whether someone contemplating that choice should be considered suicidal. Dr. Jack Kevorkian was a pivotal and controversial figure in this debate. Trained as a pathologist, he was an outspoken advocate for physician-assisted death, and he helped dozens of terminally ill patients to die, openly and in violation of the law. To many people he was a hero, someone who provided the dying with a compassionate release from their suffering. To others he was a villain who took advantage of desperate, clinically depressed people. But all agree he succeeded in placing a spotlight on the miseries endured by the dying. He engendered so much public sympathy and support that Michigan prosecutors were unable to find a jury to convict him in four separate trials. He finally was convicted of second-degree murder in a fifth trial after he videotaped himself injecting life-ending drugs into a patient with ALS (better known as Lou Gehrig's disease), a tape that was later broadcast on television.[22] But Kevorkian tapped into a deep well of discontent with care and options available at the end of life.

Indeed, people generally consider the wish of the dying to end their lives peacefully and in the comfort of their homes to be very different from the suicide of a physically healthy person who suffers from deep depression or despondency. The American Association of Suicidology (AAS), whose mission aims to understand and prevent suicide,[23] developed a detailed statement in 2017 that explained why it distinguishes aid-in-dying from suicide. In the AAS view, physician-assisted dying is not an act of self-destruction, but rather a carefully considered option, replete with safeguards against abuse, that allows the terminally ill to preserve their sense of self and dignity.[24] In an amicus curiae (friend-of-the-court) brief supporting Oregon's Death with Dignity law, a working

22. http://www.nytimes.com/2011/06/04/us/04kevorkian.html.

23. https://www.suicidology.org/about-aas/mission.

24. http://www.suicidology.org/Portals/14/docs/Press%20Release/AAS%20PAD%20Statement%20Approved%2010.30.17%20ed%2010-30-17.pdf.

group from the American Psychological Association noted: "It is important to remember that the reasoning on which a terminally ill person (whose judgments are not impaired by mental disorders) bases a decision to end his or her life is fundamentally different from the reasoning a clinically depressed person uses to justify suicide."[25]

The psychologists were responding to a legal attack on Oregon's law launched in 2001 by President George W. Bush's attorney general, John Ashcroft. Ashcroft was a deeply religious, conservative evangelical Christian who worked to bring secular law in line with his religious values. He opposed all abortion, even in cases of rape and incest, and promoted prayer in public schools.[26] Knowing that his personal views provided no legal basis to stop the Oregon law, Ashcroft argued that it violated the federal Controlled Substances Act of 1970, supposedly for allowing certain drugs to be used to expedite a patient's death. The US Supreme Court ruled in Oregon's favor in 2006, holding that the federal law was intended to prevent illegal drug dealing by physicians, and not to define state standards of medical practice.[27]

My father was not clinically depressed. However, he was very unhappy with living a life filled with pain, fatigue, shortness of breath, loss of appetite, falls, and the inability to do normal, everyday activities that gave his life meaning and pleasure. No antidepressant or counseling could restore the losses that he felt so deeply.

Dad benefited greatly from modern medical care, and he was independent and functional into his early nineties. But that medical care could not stop him from becoming so frail that it was too difficult to bathe, nor could it prevent his once-sturdy walk from devolving into an unsteady totter. Medical care could not counter the overwhelming fatigue that made it a chore to read through his beloved periodicals, nor did it help his labored breathing, which left him exhausted at the slightest

25. Brief of Amicus Curiae Coalition of Mental Health Professionals, WL 1749170 at 17, Gonzales v. Oregon, 126 S. Ct. 904 (2006) (No. 04-623).
26. http://www.nytimes.com/2001/01/14/us/ashcroft-s-life-and-judgments-are-steeped-in-faith.html.
27. https://www.oyez.org/cases/2005/04-623.

exertion. It's entirely possible that his near-constant pain could have been relieved if he had received the proper pain management from Hospice of Central Pennsylvania, but the poor care they delivered guaranteed that he would suffer until the very end. This was not how he wanted to die, nor does anyone.

Yet, many of us will face prolonged and painful dying, with escalating, costly, and ultimately ineffective medical treatment, unless we make advance arrangements otherwise. Most of us find this difficult to acknowledge and even more difficult to discuss. Media reports abound with news about the latest medical breakthroughs that treat some life-threatening disease. Acknowledging the reality of death feels like an admission of defeat, taking away someone's hope that a miracle cure awaits them. And so, most of us do not talk about it.

A Kaiser Family Foundation poll from 2015 found that the concept of discussing end-of-life issues with doctors is popular—almost 90% of the public agreed doctors should do so. In practice, though, a mere 17% of people said they actually had such a discussion. Those discussions were a little more common among seniors (27%) and those with significant disabilities or chronic illness (31%). Just a third of all those polled had ever participated in a discussion about a relative's end-of-life wishes.[28]

Most people lose the ability to make decisions about their care when they are near death, according to the 2014 report "Dying in America," issued by the health-care arm of the National Academy of Sciences.[29] However, only about 26–29% of US adults have prepared for that eventuality by signing advance directives, the legal documents that put end-of-life wishes in writing and designate a health-care proxy. Elderly Americans are much more likely to have advance directives, with reported rates as high as 71%. However, many practicing physicians say those reported high numbers do not reflect their experience with patients.[30]

---

28. https://www.kff.org/health-costs/press-release/public-strongly-favors-end-of-life-conversations-between-doctors-and-patients-with-about-eight-in-10-saying-medicare-and-other-insurers-should-cover-these-visits/.

29. http://www.nationalacademies.org/hmd/~/media/Files/Report%20Files/2014/EOL/Key%20Findings%20and%20Recommendations.pdf, p.1.

30. http://www.modernhealthcare.com/article/20150306/BLOG/303069977.

Those who don't have an advance directive leave themselves at grave risk. The "Dying in America" study warned, "A lack of an end-of-life plan, created well in advance, typically leads to prolonged hospitalization, soaring medical bills, and unnecessary pain and suffering for everyone. Too many people end up having aggressive treatment that is ineffective and expensive and doesn't contribute to the patient's quality of life."[31] A Purple Insights poll in 2014 found that one in four older Americans reported that they had received unwanted or excessive medical treatment.[32]

Most people—80%—want to be in their own homes when they die. However, 60% of Americans die in hospitals, and 20% die in nursing homes.[33] Hospitals tend not to be very good at caring for dying people. Patients there are more likely to undergo intensive procedures that cause a lot of suffering and diminish the quality of life in their final days.

What kind of care do most people want at life's end? They want to die at home with family and friends present. They want their pain and discomfort managed. They want their spiritual needs respected and honored. They want to avoid devastating their loved ones, financially or emotionally.[34]

These goals remain consistent across different cultural and ethnic groups, according to a 2015 study done by Stanford University researchers. People want to live if their quality of life is good. But when they are faced with the end of life, they want to be consulted about their wishes and to have them respected.[35]

Advance directives can help ward off unwanted end-of-life treatment, but they do not ensure your wishes will be honored. For starters, they are not much use if your health-care provider has never seen them. You need to distribute copies to all care providers and to facilities where you may receive care. Even then, it is sometimes hard to locate them in

31. https://www.nap.edu/read/18748/chapter/1.

32. https://thinkprogress.org/elderly-receive-excessive-and-expensive-medical-treatment-recent-poll-suggests-82a7fd8e3699.

33. https://palliative.stanford.edu/home-hospice-home-care-of-the-dying-patient/where-do-americans-die/.

34. http://www.asaging.org/blog/advanced-illness-care-we-can-do-better.

35. http://www.medscape.com/viewarticle/854903.

your medical record. That probably helps explain why a study from 2014 showed that even when the percentage of elderly people with advance directives increased, it made little difference in how many people were sent to the hospital and how many died there.[36]

Also, if nearby hospitals have beds offering sophisticated (and expensive) treatments, physicians will use them, even with patients at or near death.[37] A study done at Stanford University in 2014 found that while most physicians would decline aggressive medical treatment at the ends of their own lives, they deliver aggressive care to their dying patients.[38] Still, documents with end-of-life wishes can make a difference, at least in some cases. A survey of emergency physicians in 2015 showed 92% prefer having advance directives available and felt it helped them provide their patients with better care.[39]

People are more likely to have their end-of life wishes respected if a "Physician Order for Life-Sustaining Treatment" form is used along with the advance directive. The POLST,[40] as it is known in the health-care profession, was developed in Oregon twenty years ago. Most, but not all, states now use it. When my father was dying, I was completely unaware that we could request this legally powerful, highly specific physician order. His primary care provider never even mentioned it. I now wonder if having one would have prevented the worst part of his end-of-life ordeal—the five days of aggressive medical care he received before he died.

Still, a POLST is no guarantee that a person's wishes will be honored. By law, physicians are *not* legally bound to follow a patient's written wishes if they object on grounds of conscience or believe the patient's wishes are inappropriate.[41] At one of my speaking events in Florida, an audience member mentioned that a paramedic curtly informed her and

36. Maria Silveira, et al. "Advance Directive Completion by Elderly Americans: A Decade of Change." *Journal of the American Geriatrics Society*, vol. 62, no. 4, 2014, pp. 706–710.

37. http://www.dartmouthatlas.org/downloads/reports/EOL_Trend_Report_0411.pdf.

38. https://med.stanford.edu/news/all-news/2014/05/most-physicians-would-forgo-aggressive-treatment-for-themselves-.html.

39. http://www.cpbj.com/article/20151029/BLOGEXTRA/151029768/emergency-medicine-physicians-prefer-advance-directives.

40. http://polst.org/about-the-national-polst-paradigm/what-is-polst/.

41. https://www.americanbar.org/content/dam/aba/migrated/Commissions/myths_fact_hc_ad.authcheckdam.pdf.

her family that he would not honor her relative's POLST and would do everything possible to save her life.

A case from Humboldt County in California shows the lengths that the legal and medical systems will sometimes go to prevent people from having their end-of-life wishes honored. Seventy-three-year-old Dick Magney was nearing the end of his life in 2015, suffering from heart problems and liver failure, among other chronic conditions. He was dying, in pain, and decided to forego further treatment aimed at "curing" him. He, his doctors, and his wife (who was his designated health-care proxy) agreed on a course of care to reduce his pain and keep him as comfortable as possible.

However, a public health nurse for Humboldt County and her supervisors disagreed with Magney's doctor, arguing that his condition was not terminal and that he lacked the mental capacity to make his own health-care decisions. Humboldt County then asked a court to force Magney to undergo treatment and to strip his wife from her role as his medical decision-maker. The court agreed, and Magney's wishes were overridden, even though the evidence the county presented would later be described by an appeals court as inadequate, incompetent, inadmissible, and hearsay.

Ms. Magney hired a lawyer and ultimately won a court case that restored her control over her husband's health-care decisions. After his death, an appeals court held the county liable for Ms. Magney's legal fees. The county pursued its "own agenda," the court wrote, declaring that "Humboldt was not merely negligent in preparing its petition and request for an order compelling medical treatment under the Health Care Decisions Law; it knowingly and deliberately misrepresented both the law and the facts to the trial court." Calling the county's conduct "profoundly disturbing," the court said, "No reasonable person, let alone a government agency, would have pursued such a course."[42] Ms. Magney subsequently filed a civil suit against Humboldt County for forcing unwanted medical treatment on her husband in violation of his advance

42. http://www.northcoastjournal.com/media/pdf/a145981.pdf.

directive. In March 2019, four years after Dick Magney's miserable death, Humboldt County settled the lawsuit for one million dollars.[43]

A century ago, New York Appeals Court Justice Benjamin Cardozo wrote an often-quoted opinion in a case involving unwanted medical treatment. "Every human being of adult years and sound mind," he wrote, "has a right to determine what shall be done with his own body."[44]

A hundred years later, this fundamental notion of respecting human dignity and freedom of choice is still under attack. Some conservative religious leaders hold to the medieval notion that suffering like what my father endured is redemptive and will lead to salvation.[45] The National Catholic Bioethics Center explains: "Suffering and death entered the world with the sin of our first parents, but Christ's obedience to the Will of His Father can now infuse these afflictions with redemptive power . . . we can join our suffering to that of our Savior on the Cross at Calvary and thereby assist in His work of salvation for the entire world."[46]

Conservative Catholic screenwriter Barbara Nicolosi writes, "We must contradict the notion that suffering is the worst thing that can happen to a person . . . [we] must find new ways to communicate the truth of human dignity and the value of suffering."[47] Redemptive suffering is not unique to Catholics. Evangelical pastor Rick Warren writes, "Redemptive suffering is when you go through pain for the benefit of others. . . . When Jesus died on the cross, he didn't deserve to die. He went through that pain for your benefit so that you can be saved and go to Heaven."[48]

I'm left wondering to what extent religious values drove the mistreatment that the hospice and law enforcement authorities inflicted on my

43. https://www.northcoastjournal.com/humboldt/county-settles-magney-case-for-1-million/Content?oid=13561247.
44. https://wings.buffalo.edu/bioethics/schloen1.html.
45. http://www.catholicnewsagency.com/resources/sacraments/anointing-of-the-sick/st-paul-explains-the-meaning-of-suffering/.
46. http://www.ncbcenter.org/publications/end-life-guide/.
47. http://www.crisismagazine.com/2011/exposing-euthanasia-through-the-arts.
48. http://pastorrick.com/devotional/english/the-purpose-of-redemptive-suffering.

father. Though Hospice of Central Pennsylvania is a secular non-profit operation, it serves and derives its staff from a region that is culturally and religiously conservative.

Religious beliefs may not always affect how patients are treated on their deathbeds, but those beliefs come out very clearly when end-of-life issues are debated in the political arena. In Ohio in 2016, for example, Republican state senator Peggy Lehner introduced SB 165[49] to create the "Medical Order for Life-Sustaining Treatment" (MOLST) for Ohio. The bill, which had wide support of medical professionals, was modeled on similar state laws. It would list end-of-life care preferences, would need to be signed by a physician and reviewed annually, and could be revoked at any time. It passed the Ohio Senate by a vote of 30-3, despite strong opposition from abortion opponents, who claimed the bill would be used to hasten death and would promote euthanasia.[50] The bill was sent to the Ohio House of Representatives health committee in November 2016, where it failed to pass, thanks to the opposition of thirty-five Christian and pro-life organizations. Triumphant in the victory, Right-to-Life consultant Barry Sheets said, "This significant decision is the visible result of what Ohio's statewide pro-life coalition worked and prayed for."[51]

When health-care workers and medical facilities willfully ignore their loved ones' documented end-of-life wishes, some families are pushing back.[52] Lawsuits are occurring around the country in "wrongful life" cases, such as Humboldt County, California's treatment of Dick Magney. In a case out of Georgia, Jacqueline Alicea sued Doctors Hospital in Augusta and Dr. Phillip Catalano after they placed her ninety-one-year-old grandmother on a ventilator. That treatment violated her grandmother's advance directive and defied specific instructions from Ms. Alicea, who was her grandmother's health-care proxy. The hospital and Dr. Catalano claimed that they were immune from liability, but in 2016 the Georgia

49. https://www.legislature.ohio.gov/legislation/legislation-summary?id=GA131-SB-165.
50. http://www.dispatch.com/content/stories/local/2016/05/04/terminal-illness-bill.html.
51. http://www.cincinnatirighttolife.org/2016/12/09/ohios-molst-bill-dies-deserved-death/.
52. https://www.nytimes.com/2017/04/10/health/wrongful-life-lawsuit-dnr.html.

Supreme Court rejected their argument and let the case proceed. The court noted that "a clear objective of the [Georgia Advance Directive] Act is to ensure that in making decisions about a patient's health care, it is the will of the patient or her designated agent, and not the will of the health-care provider, that controls." [53]

The recent pushback by families who file wrongful life lawsuits probably helped provoke a counter-reaction from the Arizona legislature. In spring 2017, Arizona passed a law shielding health-care professionals or companies that refuse to participate in any service that they claim would result in the death of an individual. The new law also grants legal immunity to health-care workers who refuse to honor a patient's wishes or a doctor's orders because doing so would violate their moral beliefs. After heated arguments, language was added specifying the bill did not authorize performing CPR on someone with a valid do-not-resuscitate order. However, in Arizona, any other provisions of a living will can now be ignored or overridden by health-care workers who disagree with the dying person's wishes.[54] The bill was pushed by the anti-abortion group Center for Arizona Policy, whose mission is to "defend the values of life, marriage, and religious freedom."[55]

The fight to obtain end-of-life care that respects peoples' values and wishes has now leaped from the state level to the national stage. In early May 2019, the Department of Health and Human Services (HHS) Office for Civil Rights issued a final rule, known as the "conscience clause," which allows health-care professionals to decline to participate in treatments they find morally or religiously objectionable.[56] The rule has caused an uproar among patient advocacy groups, who fear it will threaten access to health care, particularly among vulnerable groups. The American Medical Association (AMA) has spoken out against the rule, and nearly twenty states and several large cities have filed a lawsuit

53. http://caselaw.findlaw.com/ga-supreme-court/1741593.html.

54. http://tucson.com/news/local/bill-protects-az-health-care-workers-who-refuse-to-help/article_eaed5244-0e30-539f-bf8f-c33a51a5e6cd.html.

55. https://www.azpolicy.org.

56. https://patientengagementhit.com/news/states-sue-hhs-moral-objections-rule-claim-care-access-violations.

against HHS to have it overturned. It's easy to envision this rule being used by some health-care professionals to refuse honoring a living will or do-not-resuscitate order, claiming that these legally executed documents violate their ethical and religious beliefs.

How can we move forward from contentious and divisive arguments over end-of-life care? It is a question with profound consequences. Of the 2.6 million people who die in the United States each year, far too many of them and their loved ones suffer unnecessarily at life's end.[57] Despite the growth of hospice care and palliative care teams in hospitals, a study funded by the National Institute of Nursing Research in 2010 found that reports of pain and other distressing symptoms at the end of life had increased.[58] Remarking on the study, Dr. Atul Gawande observed, "The amount of suffering that people endure in their last year of life is considerable. Medical care for the symptoms people experience at the end of life does not seem to have gotten better; it may have gotten worse."[59]

Regardless of whether people support a choice like medical aid-in-dying, it is clear that end-of-life care must be improved. An innovative program in LaCrosse County, Wisconsin, has had remarkable success in doing just that. The Respecting Choices program was developed in 1991 by Bernard "Bud" Hammes, PhD, a medical ethicist with the Gundersen Health System in Wisconsin.[60] Dr. Hammes based the program around high-quality discussions about people's values and preferences for their health care, not just as death approaches, but throughout life. Loved ones are included in the discussions. Instead of patients having to carry a paper copy of an advance directive or POLST, the documents are integrated into the health system and routinely updated, especially when changes in health occur. Discussions are carried out by trained

57. Joan Teno, et al. "Is Care for the Dying Improving in the United States?" *Journal of Palliative Medicine*, vol. 18, no. 8, 2015, pp. 662-666.

58. Adam Singer, et al. "Symptom Trends in the Last Year of Life from 1998 to 2010: A Cohort Study." *Annals of Internal Medicine*, vol. 162, no. 3, 2015, pp. 175-183.

59. Atul Gawande. "Quantity and Quality of Life: Duties of Care in Life-Limiting Illness." *JAMA*, vol.315, no. 3, 2016, pp. 267-269.

60. http://endumt.org/userfiles/respecting-choices.pdf.

communicators—nurses, social workers, and chaplains—rather than doctors, who may lack the necessary time or expertise.

Respecting Choices has produced impressive results. A study that looked at deaths in the region a few years after its implementation showed that 85% of the cases had advance directives, 96% of those documents were available in the medical record, and 98% of the decisions honored the written directives.[61] And it produced a positive but unexpected outcome: Medical costs dropped dramatically. The average insurance reimbursement per patient at Gundersen in the last two years of life was $18,359—almost $7,500 less than the US average. Hospital stays during that time were half of the US average of 23.5 days.[62] This does not mean care was denied or rationed. It means that the care was appropriately provided according to the person's carefully considered wishes. Satisfaction with Respecting Choices, and with other programs that integrate advance-care planning, is high.[63]

I look back on my father's death with profound regret that I was unable to ensure that his wishes were honored. He and all of us were facing an uphill battle against an institutionalized system programmed to keep people alive, a system that allows people in positions of power to determine whether their own personal beliefs or their style of medical care will override what a dying person wants. What happened to me and my father feels like a cruel modern version of the harsh English prohibition against suicide; but instead of my father's body being placed in a crossroads with a stake driven through it, he was made to suffer while he was alive—anguished over my arrest, enduring painful procedures, slapped into restraints, and dying a horrendous death. Instead of my property being confiscated by the local authorities for his actions, the state took away my livelihood, exacted a huge financial toll, and inflicted emotional agony on me and my family by prosecuting me as an accused felon. Those involved—Hospice of Central Pennsylvania, Pottsville

61. http://www.eutanasia.ws/hemeroteca/z9.pdf.
62. http://www.lifemattersmedia.org/2014/09/respecting-choices-financial-facts-figures/.
63. https://www.ncbi.nlm.nih.gov/pmc/articles/PMC2844949/.

police, the Pennsylvania attorney general, Coroner Moylan—did not prevail in court, but the message they conveyed could not have been clearer: If you want control over your own dying process in a way they do not find acceptable, there will be a huge price to pay for you and your loved ones.

Yourshaw Family photo circa 1921 – Front row L to R: my dad, Joseph (age 2, the youngest at the time); Eva; Peter; Michael; Mary. Back row L to R: John, Ann, mother Maria, father Charles, son Charles. My grandparents had four more children—Myron, Paul, Steven, and Alexander—after this photo was taken.

Graduating class of Ordnance School at General Motors Institute of Technology in Flint, Michigan, 1942. Dad is in the front row, far right. He went on to serve in the Second Infantry Division in the 293rd Ordnance Medium Maintenance Company in Europe during WWII. (Source: Collections of Kettering University)

Joseph Yourshaw in Paris during service in US Army, 1945.

Joseph Yourshaw in Pilsen, Czechoslovakia with US Army, 1945.

Marge and Joe Yourshaw on their wedding day, June 17, 1951.

Marge and Joe Yourshaw, 1978.

Yourshaw family photo, 1990 – Front row L to R: Me, Mom, Dad, sister Linda. Back row L to R: brother, Jim; sister, Virginia.

Dad and me at my parents' home in Florida, 1992.

Dad with me before my wedding, June 1994.

Dancing with Dad at my wedding, June 1994.

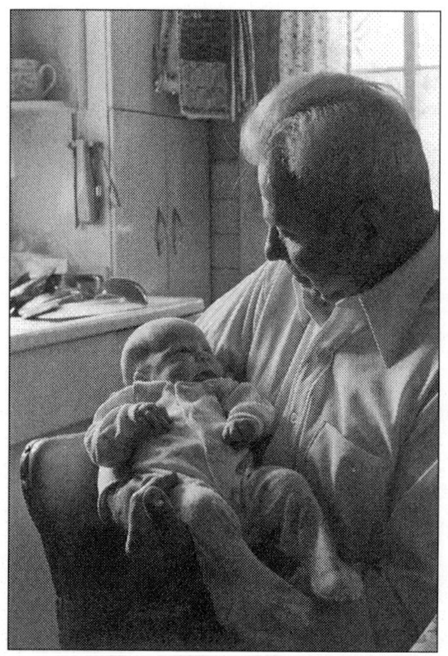
Dad holding my infant daughter Gabi, 1995.

Dad holding my infant daughter Maria, 1997.

Dad playing with my toddler Maria at a family party, 1999.

Dad working at Florida house, 2001.

Mom and Dad at Florida house, 2001.

The next set of photos are remodeling done by my dad at the Florida house when he was in his mid- to late eighties; he did all of these renovations by himself:

New deck Dad put in around the swimming pool at Florida house.

The driveway of the property in Florida was dirt and gravel when my parents bought it. Dad dug out the driveway and poured the cement by himself. This is the front side of it.

This is the back side of the completed driveway.

Arched windows – Dad broke through a solid brick wall to install these windows in the family room of the house; this was a windowless room when they bought the property.

Dad's 89th birthday in Pottsville.

Last photo taken of Mom and Dad together, October 2012.

Media filming my supporters outside Schuylkill County Courthouse in Pottsville, Pennsylvania, before my hearing on October 13, 2013. (Photo courtesy of Compassion and Choices)

CHAPTER 13

It Could Happen to You, and If It Does . . .

Justice is a machine that, when someone has once given it the starting push, rolls on of itself.

—John Galsworthy, author

BILL BENTINCK OF Palm Springs, California found out how easy it is to be jailed for simply giving love and support to someone at the end of life. A retired entomologist and medical equipment designer in Palms Springs, California, Bentinck was the caregiver for his seventy-seven-year-old wife, Linda, in 2012. She was in home hospice care, dying from end-stage chronic obstructive pulmonary disease (COPD), bedridden and completely dependent on oxygen.

After enduring steadily worse suffering for weeks on end, she had decided she could take no more. She told her husband she was going to stop using oxygen by removing the cannula, the thin oxygen supply tubes inside her nostrils.[1] Without the oxygen, her failing respiratory system could not keep her alive.

Bill asked her if she was sure about her decision. She said yes. As he sat with her and held her hand, she died. Bill waited two hours, then

1. http://articles.latimes.com/2012/jul/21/local/la-me-0722-lopez-murder-20120722.

called Linda's hospice to report what happened. The hospice workers called the county coroner, which they weren't required to do.

"The coroner then called the police," Bentinck told me, "who came to my house and told me they were arresting me." Bill was taken to jail and charged with murder. His bail was set at one million dollars.

Palm Springs police sergeant Mike Kovaleff told local press that Bentinck was arrested on suspicion of murder because assisted suicide was illegal in California and Bentinck's failure to replace the oxygen his wife had removed was a felony.[2]

Bentinck, a thin eighty-seven-year old man who needed a catheter to empty his bladder, was transferred from one jail to another in shackles. He was denied medical care as his bladder filled and his risk of a health crisis steadily grew. Finally, after twenty-four hours, he was taken to a hospital and got the catheter he required. In all, Bentinck endured three days of degrading, humiliating treatment in custody until the Riverside County district attorney decided there was insufficient evidence to support a charge of murder or aiding a suicide. The DA apparently recognized what the Palm Springs police did not: There was no crime here. Adults who are capable of making their own health-care decisions have long had the right to refuse or discontinue treatment.

If, like Bentinck, you provide care or comfort to a loved one who is near death from a terminal illness, you face dangerous legal risks for a simple reason: Many state laws banning assisted suicide are extremely vague. Police and prosecutors can exploit this legal and moral vagueness and bring charges against people whose only crime is providing compassionate care at the end of life.

The Pennsylvania law used to prosecute me refers to "A person who intentionally aids or solicits another to commit suicide," without further defining the elements of the crime. As my attorney argued to Judge Russell, the conduct covered by that law is so open to interpretation that even my elderly mother could have been charged with "assisting" a "suicide." After all, she had regularly provided the chocolate candy and soda

2. http://www.kesq.com/home/the-right-to-die_20160826082317374/59762163. In California, if a death occurs while someone is committing a felony, the person can be charged with felony murder.

that my diabetic father requested as he grew closer and closer to death. Her actions could have hastened his death by causing a diabetic coma.

Laws that are so vague are arguably unconstitutional. But these flawed assisted suicide laws remain on the books because the necessary legal challenges would take years of court appeals. Few defendants can bear the enormous costs of those appeals or want to spend so much time in legal limbo. My attorney argued that Pennsylvania's law was unconstitutionally vague, but Judge Russell was able to decide the case on other grounds, dismissing it for lack of evidence. Which is just as well—for me, anyway. Had she struck down Pennsylvania's law as unconstitutionally vague, I might have had to spend years mired in expensive legal appeals. So, these constitutionally questionable laws remain in place, which means citizens must rely on police and prosecutors to apply them in ways that avoid abuse and injustice. In many end-of-life cases, that can be a dangerous gamble.

Despite his nightmarish three-day ordeal, Bill Bentinck was fortunate—the prosecutor in his case dropped the charge relatively quickly. Huntington Williams, of Cornwall, Connecticut, was not so fortunate.

Williams was a friend to John Welles, 66, a former Marine who had built his own home on family land, was well-read, traveled widely, and was known for inventing gadgets and fixing things. Welles was dying of prostate cancer, and he refused treatment once it had spread to his spine. He had made it known that he wanted to end his life before he became completely incapacitated. A circle of friends took round-the-clock shifts caring for him in his home.

Welles decided that June 11 would be the day his suffering would end. He pulled out a rusty .38 caliber revolver and told Williams, who had arrived for his shift, what he planned to do. Respectful of Welles' wishes, Williams was concerned that the rusted gun would malfunction and maim his friend. Williams cleaned the gun, and when Welles asked him where he should aim, Williams gave his opinion. Welles then used his walker to go into his garden, and he asked Williams to leave him. Once Williams reached the driveway, he heard a gunshot. John Welles had ended his life. Williams called 911 and gave a full report to the state police.

Seven months later, prosecutors charged Williams with second-degree manslaughter, which carries a possible prison sentence of ten years. The citizens of Cornwall stood by Williams, a well-liked resident who had worked as an EMT, volunteer firefighter, and the town's civil preparedness coordinator. At each of his court appearances, his supporters packed the courtroom and the anterooms. They roundly criticized the state's attorney for filing the case and threatening such a long prison term.[3]

Despite the public outcry, the prosecutor persisted with the case. Facing up to a decade in prison if convicted at trial, Williams agreed to take a plea bargain. He received a one-year probation with accelerated rehabilitation that would leave him with no record.[4]

As Huntington Williams learned, a prosecutor has immense power to extract a plea bargain in a case with dubious foundation. His case demonstrates a truth stated as long ago as 1940, by US attorney general Robert H. Jackson, who later served as the chief US prosecutor at the Nuremberg war crime trials: "The prosecutor has more control over life, liberty, and reputation than any other person in America. His discretion is tremendous."[5]

Today, prosecutors have even more power than when Jackson spoke. Mandatory sentencing laws, passed during an era of high crime that produced widespread complaints about supposedly lenient judges, no longer allow much latitude in handing down sentences.

Federal judge Jed Rakoff has pointed out that by deciding how many and what charges to pursue, "it is the prosecutor, not the judge, who effectively exercises the sentencing power."[6] In a 2016 interview, former federal trial judge John Gleeson said, "Prosecutors have a much larger role in sentencing outcomes today, and they use their power to secure plea bargains. As a result, what was an 80% guilty plea rate has become a 97% guilty plea rate."[7]

---

3. http://www.nytimes.com/2005/03/04/nyregion/for-role-in-suicide-a-friend-to-the-end-is-now-facing-jail.html?_r=0.
4. https://www.nytimes.com/2005/04/08/nyregion/connecticut-man-74-gets-probation-for-his-role-in-a-friends.html.
5. https://www.justice.gov/sites/default/files/ag/legacy/2011/09/16/04-01-1940.pdf.
6. http://www.nybooks.com/articles/2014/11/20/why-innocent-people-plead-guilty/.
7. http://blogs.wsj.com/law/2016/03/23/an-exit-interview-with-a-federal-trial-judge/.

Those plea bargains, Judge Rakoff notes, are "negotiated behind closed doors with no judicial oversight." Says former judge Gleeson, "Our system has lost the transparency that public trials provide."

Anthony Kennedy, a recently retired US Supreme Court justice, wrote in the case *Missouri v. Frye,* "Horse trading [between prosecutor and defense counsel] determines who goes to jail and for how long. That is what plea bargaining is. It is not some adjunct to the criminal justice system; it is the criminal justice system."[8]

Most of those accused in our justice system face a terrible choice. They can plead guilty early and receive a more lenient sentence, or they can exercise their constitutional right to have a trial and face a much harsher sentence if they lose.

It's no surprise then, that innocent people, when lacking the resources needed to mount an effective defense, might take a plea deal. As Judge Rakoff notes, "The system [of prosecutorial discretion], by creating such inordinate pressures to enter into plea bargains, appears to have led a significant number of defendants to plead guilty to crimes they never actually committed."[9]

The National Registry of Exonerations confirms that concern. It reported that 2016 was a record year for exonerations, with 166 people cleared of crimes that included homicide, sexual assault, arson, robbery, and attempted murder, as well as non-violent crimes. Seventy-four of those demonstrably false convictions were the product of plea bargains. Ninety-four wrongful convictions were cases where *no crime actually occurred* [emphasis mine].[10] Many real crimes go unsolved because an innocent person, hoping to avoid even harsher prison time, has confessed to them. That problem, says Samuel Gross, the editor of the National Registry of Exonerations, is likely worst in misdemeanor courts, where nearly everyone pleads guilty.[11]

---

8. *Missouri v. Frye*, 566 U.S. 134, 143 (2012).

9. http://www.nybooks.com/articles/2014/11/20/why-innocent-people-plead-guilty/.

10. https://www.law.umich.edu/special/exoneration/Documents/Exonerations_in_2016.pdf.

11. . https://www.washingtonpost.com/opinions/the-cost-of-convicting-the-innocent/2015/07/24/260fc3a2-1aae-11e5-93b7-5eddc056ad8a_story.html?utm_term=.0c3f33466f72.

The American Bar Association standards clearly state that "the duty of the prosecutor is to seek justice, not merely to convict."[12] Yet, the pressure to win convictions is intense, because convictions are a measure of success in a prosecutor's office and lead to career advancement, promotions, and often higher political office.[13] Touting a winning record as a prosecutor is a great campaign platform for someone aspiring to serve in Congress or become governor. As of April 2017, twenty-four percent of US governors were former prosecutors,[14] and numerous former prosecutors have won election to state legislatures and Congress. Before her career imploded in scandal, the Pennsylvania attorney general who prosecuted me, Kathleen Kane, was touted as a rising star who might become the first woman from the state elected to the US Senate.[15]

In many jurisdictions, prosecutors are elected to office, so it's no surprise they are heavily influenced by the social and cultural values of the communities where they work.[16] When potential assisted suicide cases are considered, research has found that the personal beliefs of prosecutors were the most significant factor in predicting whether they would pursue the charges.[17]

According to researcher Ann Alpers, "treatment of [a terminally ill patient's] pain is never investigated unless someone knowledgeable about the treatment informs either a hospital supervisor, an ethics committee, or a local prosecutor." She also found that, with rare exceptions, "all of the cases [prosecuted or investigated] occurred in small towns or rural counties. Many of the health-care providers were outsiders—either newly arrived, members of racial or ethnic minorities, or living alternative lifestyles."[18]

---

12. http://www.americanbar.org/publications/criminal_justice_section_archive/crimjust_standards_pfunc_blk.html#1.2, Prosecution Function General Standards, Standard 3-1.2(b).

13. http://scholarlycommons.law.cwsl.edu/cgi/viewcontent.cgi?article=1176&context=cwlr, pp. 7-13.

14. States with governors that were former prosecutors in 2017 include: AR, CT, GA, MT, NJ, NM, NV, NY, NC, SC, TX, WY.

15. http://www.governing.com/topics/public-justice-safety/tns-kathleen-kane-resigns-pennsylvania.html.

16. Stephen Ziegler and Nicholas Lovrich. "Pain Relief, Prescription Drugs, and Prosecution: A Four-State Survey of Chief Prosecutors," *Journal of Law, Medicine, & Ethics*, 31 (2003): 77.

17. Alan Meisel, et al. "Prosecutors and End-of-Life Decision Making," *Archives of Internal Medicine*, 159 (1999): 1094.

18. Ibid, p.79.

My case checked three of the boxes on Alpers' risk list for end-of-life caregivers. Dad's death took place in a small town, in a rural county. The investigation was prompted by a hospice nurse who learned of Dad's morphine use from me and then informed her supervisor. And though I'd grown up in Pottsville, I had long ago moved away, to the distant big city, making me a relative "outsider."

The Pennsylvania attorney general's pursuit of baseless charges against me was all the more notable when compared to the way an earlier assisted suicide case was handled in the same county. In November 2010, Andrew Mullins, a twenty-seven-year-old Pottsville resident, was drinking beer with friends when he told them he felt his life had "no meaning." One of those friends, twenty-six-year-old David Fitting, then retrieved a loaded 9mm semi-automatic handgun from the home. Fitting handed the gun to Mullins, who shot himself in the head and died.

Fitting was arrested and charged with felony aiding suicide and misdemeanor recklessly endangering another person. He had a criminal record with prior convictions for drug possession, driving under the influence, and theft. His bail was set at $10,000 unsecured[19]—one-tenth the bail in my case. Facing the same potential sentence I did on the felony charge—ten years in prison—Fitting agreed to a plea bargain. The Schuylkill County district attorney dropped the felony aiding suicide charge and let Fitting plead guilty to reckless endangerment and possessing an instrument of crime. He was put on probation for twenty-three months and ordered to perform twenty hours of community service.[20] His sentence was remarkably lenient, because the case seems like an appropriate application of Pennsylvania's law against aiding suicide.

I have often wondered if the way the prosecution handled Fitting's case had something to do with our society's enthusiasm for owning guns and our elected officials' indifference to the widespread gun violence that results from those firearms. More than 30,000 gun deaths occur in the United States each year, and more than 60% of those deaths are

19. http://republicanherald.com/news/man-wanted-in-shooting-death-arraigned-1.1116981.

20. https://ujsportal.pacourts.us/DocketSheets/CPReport.ashx?docketNumber=CP-54-CR-0000630-2011.

suicides.[21] Those suicides, it seems, are just an unfortunate price to be paid for the right of Americans to own some 300 million guns. Perhaps we'd know more about how to prevent suicides by gun in our country if the US Congress had not severely restricted any federally funded research on gun deaths for two decades, from 1997 to 2018.[22]

In August 2013, Michael Kent, a physician from Commerce Township, Michigan, hosted a visit from his parents, who lived out of state. According to court records, his father, Rick, had been seriously ill and became much worse while staying at his son's home. Dr. Kent found his father unresponsive on the morning of September 1. Following his father's stated and written desire to forgo life-prolonging treatment, Dr. Kent stayed with his father until he died later that day. His wife then notified non-emergency dispatch to report the natural death.

EMTs arrived twenty minutes later. Unfortunately for the Kents, they were unable to provide the father's advance directive, because he'd left it at his home. Without the advance directive, the EMTs claimed that they had to "do everything they could for the patient."

Dr. Kent forcefully objected to any efforts to resuscitate his father—as a physician, he knew his father had died. Kent told the EMTs and the Oakland County sheriff's deputies, who had also responded, that he would not allow them "to assault his dead father."

The deputies ordered Dr. Kent to calm down. Still worried the EMTs would try to shock his dead father back to life, he continued to yell at them. Though he was standing against a wall with his hands raised, sheriff's deputies tasered him and put him in handcuffs. EMTs then attached his father to an external defibrillator, saw nothing but a flat line (indicating no heartbeat), then pronounced him dead.

21. https://www.nytimes.com/2017/01/09/opinion/the-hidden-gun-epidemic-suicides.html?emc=edit_th_20170109&nl=todaysheadlines&nlid=22551737&_r=0.

22. http://www.npr.org/sections/health-shots/2015/12/08/458952821/congress-still-limits-health-research-on-gun-violence. The ban was lifted by legislation passed in March 2018: https://www.npr.org/sections/health-shots/2018/03/23/596413510/proposed-budget-allows-cdc-to-study-gun-violence-researchers-skeptical.

Though Kent was never arrested or charged with a crime, he sued Oakland County and the deputies for excessive use of force. The deputies argued his lawsuit should be thrown out because government officials have qualified immunity from civil damages. Dr. Kent has prevailed in his lawsuit thus far, with the US 6th Circuit Court of Appeals rejecting the deputies' attempt to dismiss the case.[23]

As Kent learned, end-of-life caregivers can endure horrifying treatment by the authorities even when they are not prosecuted.

If you are prosecuted, you find yourself in a system that takes care of its own. The magistrate district judge handling my case, James K. Reiley, had been arrested by Pottsville police for drunk driving while he was in office. He was allowed to remain a judge and preside over criminal cases while the charge was pending, although he could not hear cases involving Pottsville police or other DUI suspects. After pleading guilty, he continued as a judge and, thanks to accelerated rehabilitative disposition, avoided jail time. Eventually he got his conviction expunged and there is no longer any record of it in the Pennsylvania court system database.[24]

If you are dragged into a criminal case, you may face, as I did, the phenomenon known as "testilying"—sworn court testimony delivered by police who are lying. In my case, police captain Durkin's criminal complaint included the made-up claim that "[the] defendant told me that her father had asked her for all his morphine so he could commit suicide and she provided it." He repeated this falsehood at my preliminary hearing.

I discovered that this kind of police lying under oath is nothing new. Irving Younger, a criminal judge in New York, wrote a half century ago, "Every lawyer who practices in the criminal courts knows that police perjury is commonplace."[25] At that time, US cities like New York were dealing with widespread crime and unrest, while the US Supreme Court

23. http://www.opn.ca6.uscourts.gov/opinions.pdf/16a0003p-06.pdf.

24. http://articles.mcall.com/2008-07-23/news/4148357_1_president-judge-william-baldwin-pennsylvania-court-blood-alcohol.

25. http://users.soc.umn.edu/~samaha/cases/irving_younger.htm.

was recognizing stronger constitutional rights for criminal defendants. Between dealing with criminals in the streets and new court-imposed limits on police tactics, Judge Younger wrote, police officers "see themselves as fighting a twofront war. . . . All's fair in this war, including the use of perjury." Sticking to the truth would allow bad actors to go free.

Though Judge Younger wrote his words decades ago, police lying continues to afflict the criminal justice system. "Police officer perjury in court to justify illegal dope searches is commonplace," wrote former San Francisco police chief Peter Keane in 2011. Narcotics officers intentionally lying under oath, he said, "is the routine way of doing business in courtrooms everywhere in America."[26]

But the lying is not limited to drug cases. In fall of 2012, the district attorney in the Bronx, New York found that police were routinely lying about arrests they made for trespassing at public housing projects.[27]

Why do some officers lie? Because they can. They know that judges believe them. Juries believe them. As Michelle Alexander, author of *The New Jim Crow: Mass Incarceration in the Age of Colorblindness* has written, most defendants know "the odds of a jury's believing their word over a police officer's are slim to none."[28] Alexander also notes that there are strong incentives for officers to keep racking up arrests and convictions, even if lying is sometimes necessary to justify them. Many police departments get government grants that reward high numbers of police stops, arrests, and convictions. Some departments use arrests and other enforcement statistics as management benchmarks, so officers may feel pressure to do what it takes to make their numbers—or else.

Lying police officers know they face little real danger of being prosecuted for perjury. The person in charge of that decision, Judge Younger noted, is the officer's "co-worker, the prosecutor." A lying police officer is as likely to be indicted for perjury, the judge wrote, "as he is to be struck down by thunderbolts from an avenging heaven."[29]

26. https://www.sfgate.com/opinion/openforum/article/Why-cops-lie-2388737.php.
27. https://www.nytimes.com/2012/09/26/nyregion/in-the-bronx-resistance-to-prosecuting-stop-and-frisk-arrests.html.
28. http://www.nytimes.com/2013/02/03/opinion/sunday/why-police-officers-lie-under-oath.html.
29. http://users.soc.umn.edu/~samaha/cases/irving_younger.htm.

What does all this mean for caregivers of a dying loved one? If you live in a small town or a religiously conservative area, you are at higher risk of legal trouble.[30] And if you do get charged, the deck is going to be stacked against you. You will find yourself confronting all the many forces that have filled US prisons with the poor and minorities. All-powerful prosecutors are tempted to do what it takes to win so they can boast to voters about their high conviction rates and advance their careers. Police and key witnesses may well lie about pivotal events. Authorities may withhold exculpatory evidence, in defiance of the protections supposedly afforded by the US Supreme Court's Brady rule.[31] Few defendants can mount an effective defense because they can't afford the astronomical cost of hiring their own attorney and experts.

This heavy tilt to the scales of justice produces a tidal wave of plea bargains, sometimes by those who are innocent. With all that, it's no wonder the United States has the largest prison population in the world. The United States has 5% of the world's people and 25% of the world's prison population. About 2.2 million Americans are incarcerated in American jails and prisons, and as many as one in three Americans have some type of criminal record.[32]

I was lucky compared to most people who are charged with crimes in our country. I am white, educated, and had no prior criminal record. I had the good fortune to find a highly capable and dogged defense attorney, and I was able to cobble together the $100,000 it took to fight the charges. I was free on bail pending trial, so I could help prepare my own defense.

I had tremendous support from my family, friends, co-workers, the public, and the media. I was able to stand firm and resist the prosecutor's brazen demands that I waive my preliminary hearing if I wanted any hope of being offered a plea bargain. That hearing (and the official

30. See footnotes 16 and 17.
31. https://www.law.cornell.edu/wex/brady_rule.
32. http://www.sentencingproject.org/wp-content/uploads/2015/11/Americans-with-Criminal-Records-Poverty-and-Opportunity-Profile.pdf.

transcript, which I had to pay for) provided the grounds that a higher court used to end the case against me. Without all these advantages, I would likely have been convicted for a crime I did not commit.

I remember discussing this after I returned to my nursing job, in a conversation with an African-American nursing assistant. She listened intently, then broke down in tears, hugged me, and said, "Now you know what so many of us live with."

Yes, I know.

CHAPTER 14

Don't Die on a Sunday

The enemy is not death. The enemy is needless suffering.
—James C. Salwitz, MD

IN 2013, WHEN I encouraged my dad to enroll in hospice care, I thought I was doing the right thing. Each week, my once-vibrant, hardworking, proud father was becoming weaker and frailer. At the time, my perception of hospice care was overwhelmingly favorable. Some relatives had received excellent care, ensuring that their pain and other distressing symptoms were well-treated. My father and I were expecting what the National Hospice and Palliative Care Organization says will be "quality, compassionate care" that includes "pain management, and emotional and spiritual support expressly tailored to the patient's needs and wishes," ending in a "peaceful and comfortable death."[1]

But Hospice of Central Pennsylvania failed to deliver that kind of care to my father. "If I was his [Mr. Yourshaw's] family, I would have been livid," a national expert on hospice care, Dr. Ira Byock, told Anderson Cooper during the *60 Minutes* broadcast about my case. "They were just doing the regulatory minimum for Mr. Yourshaw. And they weren't addressing his suffering to the extent it needed to be."

The only time I heard Hospice of Central Pennsylvania say anything about its treatment of my father was right after the *60 Minutes* broadcast.

1. http://www.nhpco.org/about/hospice-care.

Hospice of Central Pennsylvania CEO Gil Brown told the Harrisburg *Patriot-News* in an email:

> It pains us deeply when a patient's or family's experience is not what they had hoped it would be. We recognize that our services are provided at a very emotional time for families. Our daily work is to maintain a high standard of care and dignity for those facing end of life issues. While we stand by the quality of our care, we actively seek feedback from patients, families and other professionals to determine if there are ways we might enhance the services we provide.[2]

When I talk to audiences around the country, many people have high praise for the hospice care their loved one received. Workers from other hospices have told me they were appalled by what happened to my father and me, and they assured me such a scenario would be unthinkable where they work. I am truly heartened to hear those reports, as I fully support hospice care that delivers on what it promises. But, quite often, people tell me about traumatic hospice failures like the one our family experienced.

A former hospice nurse who heard me speak told me about the heartbreaking experience of her dying brother, whose pain was so undertreated he died in agony. Although experienced in end-of-life care, she was unable to obtain the necessary comfort care for her own family member.

A fellow nurse in the ER told me about her elderly relative, dying of leukemia, who had bruises all over his body from spontaneous bleeding under his skin. It was happening because his terminal cancer caused severe thrombocytopenia, a shortage of blood platelets, which help the blood to clot. But a hospice employee, woefully ignorant of the patient's medical condition, accused the family of abuse and threatened to report them. Another woman told me that the hospice believed that her grandfather,

2. http://www.pennlive.com/midstate/index.ssf/2014/10/he_asked_me_to_hand_him_the_bo.html.

who was dying of aggressive cancer and having unrelieved pain, was taking morphine too often and had his dose cut back from once an hour to once every three hours. Still others have told me of threats by hospice employees to call the police on family caregivers who they felt were using too much pain medicine for their loved ones who were suffering.

While awaiting the court ruling that would end my case, I came across a disturbing comment that a reader posted on a *New York Times* article about medical aid-in-dying. The reader had been with his ninety-two-year-old father as he died, in the middle of the afternoon, the patient "screaming in fear and distress," despite being in hospice care. "I have since heard, without asking, of dozens of hospice failures to provide comfort to those in desperate need," he wrote. "As good as [hospice care] might often be, I think one of the great untold stories is how often it is not."[3]

Since he wrote that, a special investigation by Kaiser Health News brought national attention to many of those untold stories. Entitled, "No One Is Coming: Hospice Patients Abandoned At Death's Door," the October 2017 report found that "The hospice care that people expect—and sign up for—sometimes disappears when they need it most. Families across the country, from Alaska to Appalachia, have called for help in times of crisis and been met with delays, no-shows and unanswered calls."[4]

The first hospice in the United States opened in 1974 in Connecticut. By 2015, more than 5,500 hospices were serving more than 1.65 million people.[5] That spectacular growth has been made possible largely by Medicare coverage, which pays for 90% of all hospice care in the United States.[6]

To enroll in hospice, patients must have no more than six months to live, and they must end all attempts to cure their fatal condition. Some patients balk at entering hospice care, as it implies that they must give up hope of extending their lives. However, patients may no longer have

3. https://www.nytimes.com/2014/02/08/us/easing-terminal-patients-path-to-death-legally.html.
4. https://khn.org/news/no-one-is-coming-hospice-patients-abandoned-at-deaths-door/.
5. Caroline Mayer. *Kaiser Health News*, January 27, 2015.
6. https://www.researchandmarkets.com/research/689v7r/home_care_market.

to choose between trying to prolong life or getting comfort care through hospice. In January 2016, Medicare began testing a pilot that allows hospice patients to continue treatment for advanced cancer, COPD (chronic obstructive pulmonary disease), congestive heart failure, or HIV/AIDS.[7] My father knew his end was near and only wanted to be comfortable, so this new option wouldn't have made any difference to him.

The "compassionate care" promised by hospice is for both patients and their loved ones. A team that includes physicians, nurses, social workers, spiritual counselors, grief counselors, home health aides, and even volunteers is supposed to work together to meet the patient's medical needs and provide psychological support to both patients and their caregivers.

Hospice services do make it easier to care for a patient at home, but it's still a heavy responsibility. If hospice patients need help with dressing, bathing, or hygiene, Medicare will pay for occasional home health aide visits. (My father was too uncomfortable having a stranger help with those intimate needs, so he declined that service until near the end, and my mother did the best she could to help him.) However, Medicare will not pay for daily or round-the-clock care delivered at home. For that, families need to hire a private nurse or home health aide at their own expense. A Massachusetts woman told the *New York Times* she was surprised to learn that the hospice expected her to administer her father's morphine. Lacking any medical training, she and her family decided to hire a full-time private nurse instead. "People should understand that in-home hospice means that for much of the time you are on your own," she told the *Times*.[8]

Patients who already live in a nursing home or assisted-living facility may receive hospice care there. A hospice patient who is having a medical crisis or intense needs can, for a limited time, be transferred to a more intensive level of care. It's important to know in advance how to invoke that option and how the hospice will follow through on it.[9]

---

7. http://www.hhs.gov/about/news/2015/07/20/cms-announces-medicare-care-choices-model-awards.html. See also https://www.nytimes.com/2015/07/22/upshot/medicare-to-try-a-blend-of-hospice-care-and-treatment.html.

8. https://www.nytimes.com/2018/01/15/opinion/hospice-care.html.

9. Caroline Mayer. "Learning About Hospice Should Begin Long Before You Are Sick," *Kaiser Health News*, Jan. 27, 2015.

Despite my health-care background, I was woefully uninformed about the potential problems with hospice. When my father's primary physician referred us to Hospice of Central Pennsylvania, I never thought to consider any other one, even though there was at least one other option. I just assumed the hospice would do what it was supposed to do. Now I realize that you need to choose a hospice as carefully as you choose a doctor.

I have been told by audience members at my speaking events that their dying loved ones were *assigned* to a particular hospice by a hospital or nursing home. But if you live in an area with more than one hospice, you are free to choose the one you want. (For tips on choosing and using a high-quality hospice, see Appendix B.)

The hospice team is required to prepare a plan of care, which is supposed to be tailored to the needs and values of the patient, and the patient (or a representative) is supposed to understand and approve it. Caregivers should insist on being included in this part of the process.

In my father's second hospice enrollment, the vast majority of the care plan covered the long list of comfort medications he was prescribed to take—13 drugs in all. My mother and I were never told about all those medications, and we were never told that the hospice decided to withhold all of them. The hospice apparently thought my father refused all prescription medications. However, his intention was to refuse medications that would prolong his life, not ones that would ease his suffering—a critical misunderstanding that would have been cleared up if the hospice had discussed the matter with me or my mother.

Care plans are supposed to be revised as necessary, which was obviously something that didn't happen with my father. He repeatedly complained of pain, but hospice personnel regularly filed reports claiming he was "comfortable despite pain" (a classic oxymoron) and said that he "expressed symptom relief at desired level 75% of the time or greater." However, a social worker who evaluated him had more accurately noted, "no observable progress. Expresses little to no relief of symptoms to desired level. Expresses little to no hope in attaining symptom relief."[10]

---

10. Hospice record, January 18, 2013.

The social worker's report should have triggered swift revisions in my father's plan of care, a process that his caregivers, my mother and I, should have been involved with.

Federal standards require hospices to have critical services—either a nurse or doctor and whatever drugs the patient might need—available round the clock, 365 days a year. But the Kaiser Health investigation uncovered case after case where families reported trouble getting a nurse or doctor in the last critical days or hours of a loved one's life. An on-call nurse turned off her cell phone at five P.M. and missed urgent calls. In another case, the on-call nurse was out sick on short notice. In another, the one available nurse was already taking care of another patient. A dying man in Alaska waited six days for the liquid pain medicine he needed, because the hospice's prescribing doctor was unavailable. In a federally supervised study, one in five hospice families reported that hospice help did not always arrive when needed.[11] More than one surviving family member, traumatized by a loved one's ordeal, has said, "Don't die on a Sunday," because that's when hospice staffing is extremely thin.

Experts in the hospice industry admit that hospices vary greatly in quality of care. They also acknowledge that for survivors who witness a bad death of a loved one, the devastating effects can endure for the rest of their lives.[12] An executive at a well-regarded western US hospice told me that their care fails to meet patient expectations in a quarter of their cases. I was once invited to talk to a large hospice's ethics committee, as the hospice was alarmed at the increasing number of suicides among area hospice patients. Hospice patients whose needs are being met do not resort to suicide.

Federal law has pages of detailed standards that hospices must meet to qualify for payments through Medicare or Medicaid, but it's difficult to find out how well hospices follow those standards.[13] The job of

11. https://khn.org/news/no-one-is-coming-hospice-patients-abandoned-at-deaths-door/.

12. https://www.washingtonpost.com/news/business/wp/2014/09/03/is-one-hospice-the-same-as-any-other-no-why-its-important-to-choose-carefully/?utm_term=.1c702069f2eb.

13. https://www.washingtonpost.com/business/economy/quality-of-us-hospices-varies-patients-left-in-dark/2014/10/26/aa07b844-085e-11e4-8a6a-19355c7e870a_story.html?tid=a_inl.

monitoring hospices falls to state health departments, using federal funding provided by Medicare. The quality of state oversight varies greatly. Oregon has had strong standards and has carefully enforced them since the mid-1980s.[14] Other states rely on Medicare funding to monitor hospices, and until late 2014, Medicare paid for inspections only once every six years. Some hospices went as long as eight years between inspections. Nursing homes, by contrast, are inspected about once a year, and home health agencies about once every three years.

In October 2014, Congress passed the Impact Act, which requires hospice inspections every three years and pledged $70 million over ten years to pay for those inspections. Welcoming the tighter oversight, the president of the National Hospice and Palliative Care Organization, J. Donald Schumacher, said, "a lot of things can go wrong when no one's looking."[15]

But even when inspections occur, the focus is usually on proper record-keeping rather than evaluating the quality of care that patients actually receive. Typically, inspectors simply review documents about a sample of cases, although they may make some home visits.[16] I strongly suspect that some of the false charting in my father's hospice records—"comfortable despite pain" and "expressed symptom relief at desired level 75% of the time or greater"—was an attempt to make his care look good on paper to a health department reviewer.

If you want to research a particular hospice, you can probably find some inspection results on your state health department's website, but you may have trouble making sense of what's there. My home state, Pennsylvania, posts hospice inspection reports on the internet, but to the average person, they are mostly baffling bureaucratic jargon. You are likely to find out that the hospice is "in compliance with the requirements of 42 CFR, Part 418, Subparts A, C & D, Conditions of Participation:

14. Per conversation with Ann Jackson, former executive director and chief executive officer of Oregon Hospice Association.

15. http://newoldage.blogs.nytimes.com/2014/10/06/extra-scrutiny-for-hospices/?_r=0.

16. https://www.washingtonpost.com/business/economy/is-that-hospice-safe-infrequent-inspections-means-it-may-be-impossible-to-know/2014/06/26/e258e880-eaa4-11e3-b98c-72cef4a00499_story.html?utm_term=.9fa9dfd8f244.

Hospice Care" and not much more.[17] Florida does a better job, offering much more consumer-friendly information in a comprehensive hospice report, which includes three quality indicators based on family and caregiver surveys.[18]

The mere fact that a state health department and the Medicare program say a hospice is qualified to operate does not guarantee good quality care. Closing a bad hospice is a drastic step, rarely taken. Federal records show that inspectors found deficiencies in more than half of the 4,453 hospices checked during the five years ending in early 2017, according to Kaiser Health News. But only seventeen hospices were terminated from Medicare during that period.

In 2010, the federal Affordable Care Act directed hospices to publicly report some information about quality. However, the job of defining exactly what information must be reported was left to the federal health-care bureaucracy. Seven years later, in August 2017, the federal government finally launched a website called Hospice Compare.[19]

At first, the site offered only self-reported data from hospices, and most of the data dealt with procedural steps rather than outcomes for patients. Researching a hospice, you could learn the percentage of patients who are asked about their treatment preferences, their values and beliefs, and whether they experience pain or shortness of breath. However, the hospice was not required to report how well it actually met those preferences and medical needs.

Hospice Compare was improved by adding a section based on surveys of family members. It covers topics such as how well the hospice manages pain and communicates with the family; whether it delivers timely help and treats the patient with respect; and whether the family would recommend the hospice. But even with those improvements, some potentially valuable information is lacking. You can find out whether patients on opioids are *offered* treatment for constipation, but you don't learn

17. https://sais.health.pa.gov/CommonPOC/content/publiccommonpoc/QAsurvey.asp?FACID=153099&PAGE=1&NAME=HOSPICE+OF+CENTRAL+PENNSYLVANIA&SurveyType=H%20&COUNTY=.

18. http://elderaffairs.state.fl.us/doea/Evaluation/2015_Hospice_Report_Final.pdf.

19. https://www.medicare.gov/hospicecompare/#.

whether patients actually get the treatment, or how well the constipation treatment works for them.

Nationally, hospices show average scores in the 75% to 90% range on measures of family satisfaction with their services. By 2018, Hospice of Central Pennsylvania scored at or slightly above national averages. But the first year of data on the site showed Hospice of Central Pennsylvania did a particularly poor job of assessing a patient's pain, doing so in only 37.2% of cases—half the national average.[20] As of 2018, Hospice Compare showed that 25% of families were not satisfied with the way Hospice of Central Pennsylvania managed the patient's pain—a sobering score, but right at the national average.

Early on, hospices were non-profit operations run by religious organizations or community groups. But hospice has become a $17 billion-a-year industry that attracts hedge funds and private equity investors. For-profit operations have come to dominate about three-quarters of the hospice field.[21] Because hospices are paid a flat daily fee for routine care, regardless of the services they deliver, they have an incentive to increase profit margins by scrimping on care for patients. In October 2016, the daily rate was $190.55 for routine home hospice care, before adjustments for geographic differences in wages.[22] Federal data shows that in 2015, for-profit hospices spent $39 a day less per patient than non-profit hospices. The average patient served by a for-profit hospice stayed in care 60% longer—105 days, versus only 65 for those in non-profit hospices.[23] The same federal report noted that in 2014, for-profit hospices made 14.5 cents on every dollar paid to them by Medicare.[24]

20. https://www.medicare.gov/hospicecompare/#about/theData.

21. https://www.washingtonpost.com/business/economy/terminal-neglect-how-some-hospices-fail-the-dying/2014/05/03/7d3ac8ce-b8ef-11e3-96ae-f2c36d2b1245_story.html?utm_term=.c1e88a9f9bd5; however, there is a small discrepancy between this figure and other reports, which place market share of for-profit hospices at 69 percent. See: https://hospicenews.com/2019/03/15/medpac-for-profits-account-for-100-percent-of-new-hospices/.

22. https://www.cms.gov/Outreach-and-Education/Medicare-Learning-Network-MLN/MLNMattersArticles/Downloads/MM9729.pdf.

23. http://www.medpac.gov/docs/default-source/reports/mar17_medpac_ch12.pdf?sfvrsn=0, p. 327.

24. Ibid, p. 336.

For-profit hospices tend to spend less on nursing care, are less likely to have sent a nurse to a patient's home in the last forty-eight hours of life, are less likely to provide crisis care for patients who need it, and are more likely to have a patient leave hospice before dying. They are more likely to serve patients in nursing homes or assisted-living facilities than in the patients' own homes, where costs are higher. For-profit hospices are three times as likely to exceed Medicare's cap on excess reimbursements. They provide a more limited range of services to patients and caregivers, have fewer professionalized staff, have worse staff-to-patient ratios, and are less likely than non-profits to care for patients with cancer diagnoses.[25] [26]

Besides rewarding hospices that scrimp on services, Medicare's flat-rate daily payment structure creates a strong incentive to bring in borderline patients because they don't need as many services and thus help yield extra profits. A warning sign of trouble on both of those fronts—lower quality of care and whether appropriate patients are enrolled—is the rate at which live patients leave hospice. It's true that some patients do drop out for legitimate reasons—they can no longer afford it, or their illnesses may not progress as rapidly as doctors predicted (as happened the first time my father entered hospice). However, a high drop-out rate can also indicate that patients or caregivers were dissatisfied or that patients who were not close to dying were inappropriately enrolled. In ten percent of Medicare-funded hospices, at least half of their patients leave before dying.[27] Florida found that for-profit hospices in the state were 50% more likely to discharge a live patient than their non-profit counterparts.[28] Those high discharge rates suggest that some providers may be exploiting the way Medicare pays for hospice care. You can check a hospice's live discharge rate and how it compares to a statewide average in the *Washington Post*'s useful "Consumer Guide to Hospice,"[29] available online.

---

25. http://www.mountsinai.org/about-us/newsroom/press-releases/major-disparities-between-for-profit-and-nonprofit-hospice-detailed-in-national-survey.
26. http://archinte.jamanetwork.com/article.aspx?articleid=1832198.
27. http://www.medpac.gov/docs/default-source/reports/mar17_medpac_ch12.pdf?sfvrsn=0.
28. http://elderaffairs.state.fl.us/doea/Evaluation/2015_Hospice_Report_Final.pdf.
29. http://www.washingtonpost.com/wp-srv/special/business/hospice-quality/.

Rapid growth in the hospice industry, with its potential for big profits, has produced steady turnover in ownership, as medical care conglomerates and private equity investors buy up hospice companies.[30] Between 1999 and 2009, more than 40% of hospices changed ownership at least once. Patients and their families may research a hospice's past record, only to learn that the ownership has recently changed, making it hard to predict the quality of care it will deliver.

Disputing the notion that for-profit hospices are inherently worse, Peter Brunnick, president and CEO of Hospice and Palliative Care Charlotte Region, told the *Washington Post*, "There are good for-profit hospices just as there are bad non-profit hospices."[31] (As for the second half of his statement, I'd have to agree; Hospice of Central Pennsylvania is a non-profit.) For-profits claim that Wall Street money allows them to invest more in equipment and technology, which in turn will improve care for patients.[32] But how can technology and equipment replace a caring nurse, social worker, or spiritual care adviser? People view dying as an overwhelming emotional and spiritual experience, a transcendent life passage as profound as birth. They want empathy, understanding, and compassion. They want their dignity honored. That takes a caring, human connection. No machine invented can substitute for that.

As hospice use becomes more widespread, the care being delivered at the end of life should be improving. However, it seems to be getting worse, according to a study in the *Journal of Palliative Medicine*. In surveys of bereaved family members or a close friend of the person who died, the share of cases where end-of-life care was "excellent" dropped nearly ten percentage points. In 2000, it was 56.7% and by 2011-13, it fell to 47%, though the likelihood of getting "excellent" end-of-life care was higher for those in hospice.[33]

30. https://www.washingtonpost.com/business/economy/2014/12/26/a7d90438-692f-11e4-b053-65cea7903f2e_story.html.

31. https://www.washingtonpost.com/news/business/wp/2014/09/03/is-one-hospice-the-same-as-any-other-no-why-its-important-to-choose-carefully/.

32. https://www.washingtonpost.com/business/economy/2014/12/26/a7d90438-692f-11e4-b053-65cea7903f2e_story.html.

33. J. Teno, et al. "Is care for the Dying Improving in the United States?" *Journal of Palliative Medicine*, April 1, 2015.

A survey by the Kaiser Family Foundation, published in April 2017, confirmed the discouraging trend. It found that 54% of respondents rated medical care at the end of life as fair or poor. Nearly seven of every eight patients in the survey reported that they want more say in their treatment options at life's end. Living as long as possible ranks at the *bottom* of the wish list.[34] As the authors of the earlier study in the *Journal of Palliative Care* concluded, "substantial unmet needs in end-of- life care remain."

Given my family's own miserable hospice experience and the anecdotal reports I'd heard, I wondered just how pervasive poor-quality hospice care is, and how deeply the oversight agencies were scrutinizing hospice performance. A critical forty-one-page report released by the Office of Inspector General (OIG) of the US Department of Health and Human Services in July 2018 validated my concerns. The OIG report revealed that some hospices provide poor-quality care, fail to provide needed services, and do not effectively treat pain or other end-of-life symptoms. Spanning 2005 to 2017, the OIG investigation uncovered cases of fraud, kickbacks, false documentation, and inappropriate enrollment of people who were not terminally ill, leading to multiple criminal and civil court cases. As the report noted, all care related to the terminal illness *must* be provided by the hospice, and it cited several instances of hospice failure at the inpatient care level, including a 101-year-old hospice patient with uncontrolled pain for sixteen days, where the hospice failed to change his medication until the last day, and a seventy-year-old patient who was billed for seventeen days of inpatient hospice care, yet who was never seen by the hospice. Instead, the hospice called the patient's family to monitor his progress. Inpatient hospice care is considered a high level of care and is billed at $735 per day.[35]

The OIG noted the Centers for Medicare and Medicaid Services (CMS) does not provide enough data about hospice quality to allow patients and their families to make an informed choice, and that the hospices themselves often gave only partial or incorrect information

34. http://kff.org/report-section/views-and-experiences-with-end-of-life-medical-care-in-the-us-findings/.
35. https://oig.hhs.gov/oei/reports/oei-02-16-00570.pdf, p. 1–4.

about the hospice benefit.[36] The report authors recommended a number of improvements to the provision of hospice care, stressing the need for better monitoring and oversight.

A year later, in July 2019, the OIG followed up with another report on hospice quality issues.[37] The two-part report, covering five years of data collection from 2012–2016, examined deficiencies in hospice care and specific instances of harm uncovered by surveyors from state agencies and accreditation organizations. Findings in the first part of the report showed 87% of the 4,563 hospices surveyed in this time period had at least one deficiency in quality care, and many had multiple deficiencies. The most prevalent deficiencies involved inadequate care planning, poorly trained and managed hospice aides, and insufficient assessments of hospice patients' needs. Twenty percent of the hospices had deficiencies so serious that the OIG considered them "poor performers."

The second part of the 2019 report detailed cases of patients egregiously harmed by their hospice providers.[38] These included:

- A patient with Alzheimer's who developed pressure ulcers to both heels two weeks after enrolling in hospice care. The ulcers progressively worsened until the patient developed gangrene, requiring hospitalization and amputation of the left leg.
- A patient under hospice care who was found to have maggots infesting the insertion site of his feeding tube. He, too, had to be transferred to a hospital for treatment.
- A hospice medical director who refused to order the appropriate medications for a patient with uncontrolled pain. His family filed a complaint, which the hospice failed to properly document, investigate, or address.
- A hospice that sent a single, inadequately trained aide to assist a patient who required two people and a mechanical lift to transfer

36. Ibid, p. 7–9.

37. https://oig.hhs.gov/oei/reports/oei-02-17-00020.pdf?utm_source=summary-page&utm_medium=web&utm_campaign=OEI-02-17-00020-PDF.

38. https://www.oig.hhs.gov/oei/reports/oei-02-17-00021.pdf?utm_source=summary-page&utm_medium=web&utm_campaign=OEI-02-17-00021-PDF.

> her from a wheelchair to her bed. The aide attempted to transfer the patient by picking her up under her arms. She fell out of the aide's grip onto the floor, causing her right leg to fracture. She died ten days later.

None of the hospices in these and other incidents detailed in the report faced any penalties for the harm they caused to patients under their care. The only enforcement tool CMS has to hold hospices accountable is termination of Medicare participation, an action that is rarely used. Some recommendations put forth by OIG to address hospice quality of care issues include amending the law to allow penalties for poor performance (such as monetary fines and withholding of future payments), and including on Hospice Compare the findings of surveyors from state and accrediting agencies, as well as a listing of complaints filed against individual hospices.

Hospice industry organizations expressed alarm at the information in the reports, and responded by saying that the incidents detailed in them are rare and not representative of the care provided by the majority of hospices.[39] I would like to believe that is true, and hope that hospice companies that provide high-quality care will advocate for greater availability and transparency of quality care data. Consumers desperately need this information to distinguish quality hospice providers from the poor performers.

At one of my presentations, a person who volunteers at a hospice told me that we need to show support for hospice and not be critical. I understand that talking about what happened to our family may make hospice workers uncomfortable, but it was hardly an isolated experience, as the OIG reports demonstrate. Staying silent will not help anybody.

While attending legislative hearings on medical aid-in-dying proposals in several states, I have heard opponents say again and again that aid-in-dying is unnecessary. Proper hospice and palliative care, they assert, can make the dying comfortable in nearly every situation. In theory, that

39. https://www.nhpco.org/nhpco-responds-to-new-oig-reports-on-hospice-care/.

may be true—but at those same legislative hearings, I witnessed people who waited for hours to testify about their loved ones' agonizing deaths, despite receiving hospice care. The evidence is undeniable: People who are under hospice care still suffer.

My father, fiercely independent and strong-willed, enjoyed his life when it was filled with purpose and meaning. He looked at his accomplishments with satisfaction and pride, whether it was surviving a terrible war, building his own business, raising and providing for his family, building or inventing things to make life easier or more comfortable, or relaxing with his favorite reading materials. As the end of life approached, he was not only in constant pain but he lost his ability to engage in activities that defined who he was. The very foundation of his identity was rapidly slipping away from him. That loss of control, dignity, and purpose can cause as much or more suffering than physical pain.

Dad was hardly unusual in wanting to have some control over the end of his life. When people who were dying were asked how they defined "dying well," the overwhelming majority—94%—said their top concern was making sure their preferences were honored—preferences about how, where, and when they died; who was present at the time of death; what types of medical treatment they wanted (or didn't want); and funeral arrangements. Being pain-free was the second most common concern, followed by having their emotional and spiritual needs met.[40]

Long before the Kaiser special report on widespread failures in hospice care, Dr. Ira Byock told *60 Minutes* that my father's case "is emblematic of how we are failing elders, chronically ill people, vulnerable people in America. We are not treating people's suffering. We are making them feel undignified. Ask any boomer who's cared for their parents. They'll tell you that even for those of us who are doctors and nurses, it's really, really hard to get the basics of care for your frail loved one met."

40. Emily Meier, et al. "Defining a Good Death (Successful Dying): Literature Review and a Call for Research and Public Dialogue," *American Journal of Geriatric Psychiatry,* April 2016, pp. 261-271.

Physicians Jennifer Brokaw and Robert Kane would certainly agree. Writing in *TIME* on September 29, 2016, they said, "We are two experienced physicians who were responsible for our loved ones in long-term care facilities. Both of our experiences left us deeply concerned about the ability of ordinary, non-medical people to receive quality, dignified care at the ends of their lives."[41] At my talks, even people who work in a hospice have told me that their own family members had a distressing experience with hospice care. As Drs. Brokaw and Kane wrote in *TIME*, "If even people like us—with all our resources and personal connections—could not get the acute medical and long-term care that honors the wishes of patients and families to have a gentle and dignified end, the system is broken."[42]

All of us face the risk of having our most personal and intimate life decisions placed under the control of those who may not agree with what we want or who try to impose their value systems on others. Preparing well ahead of time—with advance directives, binding medical orders that are periodically updated, along with regularly talking to loved ones about end-of-life preferences—can help improve the odds of ensuring your wishes are honored. Choosing a hospice carefully, interviewing the hospice, thoroughly researching its performance and how it upholds your rights and preferences as a patient, will also help.

But for some who see a gruesome end coming—with intense suffering at a time when they may be physically unable to do anything for themselves—the only option, in most of the country, is to wait until the end is near and then try to hasten death by agreeing to end all life-sustaining care, sometimes even refusing food and water. Imposing such a harsh choice simply prolongs their suffering and inflicts more agony on their caregivers. Those patients deserve the freedom to make other end-of-life choices before they are too debilitated to act on them—something the voters in the state of Oregon recognized in the mid-1990s. For terminally ill patients who seek a more dignified death, the state of Oregon has led the way.

41. http://time.com/4513741/end-of-life-care-concerns/.
42. Ibid.

CHAPTER 15

Oregon Shows the Way

It has often been said, that it is not death, but dying, which is terrible.

—Henry Fielding

ASK PEOPLE WHAT they would want if they knew their death were rapidly approaching, and one theme stands out among the answers: They want to preserve their autonomy. At my speaking events, people tell me they want to be allowed to "go the way they want to go." They do not want to surrender control over their last days to huge, impersonal hospitals and doctors they may not even know. They don't want someone telling them that only a certain way of dying is acceptable. They don't want to die among a bunch of strangers. They want to be in their own homes, where their surroundings are familiar. They want government officials and medical authorities to butt out of their personal decisions. One person told me, "I don't want to go to some damned hospital and put up with their rules. It's *my* life, and it's *my* death."

In years past, a few desperate Americans who were facing death felt so strongly about controlling their own fates that they resorted to extreme measures, testing the boundaries of anti-suicide laws. In doing so, they placed those who helped them in serious legal danger.

Dozens chose to consult Dr. Jack Kevorkian and use his "suicide machine," which allowed them to take a fatal dose of drugs. Kevorkian, an early advocate of medical aid-in-dying, was put on trial four times and was freed four times, before Michigan prosecutors finally convicted him of second-degree murder. Spending eight years in prison, he was released only after promising not to help any other dying patients end their lives.[1]

Other patients chose to choreograph their own exits from life, with help from family members. Velma Howard of Joplin, Missouri was one of them. In 1996, she was age seventy-six and suffering from amyotrophic lateral sclerosis (ALS), commonly known as Lou Gehrig's disease. One of the grimmest fatal diseases known to humankind, ALS gradually paralyzes more and more parts of the body, eventually leaving the patient alert, conscious, and totally dependent on others for survival.

Howard chose her fiftieth wedding anniversary for the day she would end her suffering, surrounded by those she loved. Seeking a peaceful and painless death, she decided to use instructions from Derek Humphry's controversial 1991 best-seller, *Final Exit*. Her husband and son mixed sleeping pills and alcohol in juice, then arranged the room so she could reach a plastic bag to put over her head with a rubber band to secure it. The sedatives were intended to help her pass out before she died from denying herself oxygen.

After her death, Mrs. Howard's husband and son were arrested and charged with voluntary manslaughter, though their only "crime" was helping a loved one fulfill her end-of-life wishes. The case never went to trial, and the prosecutor ultimately dismissed the case.[2]

Thomas Meyer, of Connecticut, faced harsher consequences. In 2006, his ninety-seven-year-old mother, Elizabeth, had decided she had suffered enough and was ready to end her own life—something she had said many times she intended to do. She, too, was familiar with the advice detailed in Humphry's book, *Final Exit*. Meyer had a close relationship with his mother, faithfully visiting her daily, and when she pleaded for his help, he agreed. After she died, he contacted police and confessed to helping her carry out her wishes. Meyer was charged with second-degree

1. https://www.nytimes.com/2011/06/04/us/04kevorkian.html.

2. http://articles.chicagotribune.com/1996-04-16/news/9604160104_1_9th-circuit-velma-howard-rulings.

manslaughter and was convicted. He avoided prison time, but his felony record prevented him from finding employment and housing.[3]

Howard and Meyer chose to take such desperate measures because, where they lived (Missouri and Connecticut, respectively), the idea that doctors might provide the terminally ill with well-regulated and carefully controlled ways to hasten their deaths was considered too radical. The medical profession was expected to fight death with all the power it could muster, no matter how harsh a toll it might take on a dying patient. And when all hope was gone, the patient would simply have to wait for death to come.

In the past couple of decades, social attitudes toward the choices that terminally ill patients are allowed to make have begun to shift—and the state of Oregon has led the way. Its Death with Dignity Act was the nation's first law to authorize medical aid-in-dying. Passed in 1994 by voter initiative, the law was put on hold by court challenges and did not take effect until 1997, after a statewide repeal vote failed.[4] Oregon's option is available to mentally capable, terminally ill adults with a prognosis of six months or less to live. Two physicians have to agree on the terminal diagnosis. Patients must make two oral requests and a written request and, if those are approved, undergo a fifteen-day waiting period. If physicians suspect untreated depression or impaired decision-making, a mental health evaluation is required. Physicians are not required to participate if they are opposed to the law.

The documentary *How to Die in Oregon* gives an intimate look at how several people used the state's aid-in-dying law. Cody Curtis, 54, a mother of two grown children, barely survived an earlier bout with liver cancer, including an arduous six-month recovery from surgery complications that left her completely helpless. Soon after, though, her cancer came back. If surgical removal of the cancer fails, the remaining treatment options only buy a few months of extra time, while the patient endures greater pain and discomfort.

3. Connecticut public hearing testimony by Thomas Meyer in support of HB 6645, 3/20/2013.

4. https://public.health.oregon.gov/ProviderPartnerResources/EvaluationResearch/DeathwithDignityAct/Documents/history.pdf.

Soon after getting the terminal diagnosis, Curtis filled the prescription for the fatal dose of drugs. "It's very comforting to know they're right here," she said in the film. "It's whenever I decide. It's my choice when to take them and whether to take them." The movie follows Curtis as she outlived her six-month terminal diagnosis, looking surprisingly healthy to the outside world. But knowing the end would eventually come, she found that having the drugs on hand was a psychological insurance policy against future suffering.

"With Death with Dignity, you do have some control over what's going to happen. It means you can have some good times," Curtis said, referring to the Oregon law. "It gives me a chance to think about how I want to leave things with them [husband, son, and daughter] at the end."

Looking ahead to when the cancer would take root again, Curtis said that the law would indeed let her maintain her dignity. "I'm not going to die with the fluid oozing out of the pores of my legs," she said. "I'm not going to weigh 200 pounds again. I'm not going to be humiliated with losing control of my bodily functions again."

Eventually her liver began to fail, and her abdomen filled with unmanageable amounts of fluid. A pathological stew, the equivalent of three 2-liter bottles of soda, squeezed her internal organs causing intense pain and pressing against her diaphragm, leaving her barely able to breathe. The fluid buildup, her doctor said, is like going from not being pregnant to nine months pregnant in just a week.

In her last couple of days, the pain was so intense that Curtis was taking 25 milligrams of morphine an hour. (That's ten times the dose, and six times the frequency, of what my father was provided the second time he enrolled in hospice.) "I'm suffering," Curtis says on camera, but thanks to the Oregon law, "There's a door I can open." Explaining her decision to use the fatal prescription instead of letting cancer take its course, she said, "I wasn't going to just drift away. It was going to be excruciating. . . . I understand there's a kind of dignity in suffering, but there's a certain grace in accepting the inevitable."

Curtis's daughter, Jill, drew comfort from knowing that her mom was able to die at home, on her own terms, surrounded by loved ones. "If she had died at the hospital, it really would have felt like she was pulled out of our hands," Jill Curtis said. "Because you're still fighting to keep her, and that's what hospitals are about, that fight to keep people alive."

The state of Oregon keeps detailed statistics on how the law is performing. Through 2018, a total of 2,217 terminally ill people had prescriptions written for fatal doses, and 1,459 of them used the medicine to accelerate their deaths.[5] Of patients who chose Death with Dignity during 2018, most (79.2%) were sixty-five years or older. The median age at death was seventy-four years. As in previous years, those using the law to die on their own terms were mostly white (97%) and well-educated (nearly half had at least a college degree). Like Cody Curtis, most patients had cancer (62.5%), while much smaller numbers had neurological disease (14.9%) or terminal heart disease (9.5%). Most patients (87.5%) died at home, and most (90.5%) were enrolled in hospice care. Ninety-nine percent had some form of health-care insurance.

When Oregon voters passed Death with Dignity, it prompted health-care providers throughout the state to collaborate in improving end-of-life care. They worked to increase access to hospice care, and reimbursement to hospice providers was improved. Coverage under the Oregon Health Plan, which serves low-income residents, was extended. Several Oregon hospitals developed and expanded palliative care teams, which provide comfort for the terminally ill and for other patients with life-threatening illnesses. The state's medical profession also recognized that doctors and nurses needed better education in comfort care and end-of-life issues.[6]

Oregon's law "has called attention to the needs of all dying people," not just the small percentage who choose aid-in-dying, according to bioethicist Arthur Caplan. By prompting improved palliative care for

---

5. https://www.oregon.gov/oha/PH/PROVIDERPARTNERRESOURCES/EVALUATION RESEARCH/DEATHWITHDIGNITYACT/Documents/year21.pdf.

6. M. Lee and S. Tolle. "The Silver Lining," *Archives of Internal Medicine.* January 15, 1996, p.267-269.

the terminally ill, Caplan wrote in 2005, "The Oregon law probably has benefited many more people than have actually used it."[7]

By 2008, Oregon ranked high in almost all measures of end-of-life care. Its at-home death rate was among the highest. No state had a higher rate of patients who prepared advance directives for end-of-life medical treatment.[8] Oregon is in the top tier of states for the rate of hospice use and is among the states having the lowest rates of questionable hospice stays (those shorter than a few days, or longer than 180 days, or where the patient withdraws before death).[9] One indicator of poor hospice care—the number of suicides among hospice patients—had been quite low in Oregon, but after the state enacted aid-in-dying, the suicide rate fell to zero, according to Ann Jackson, former executive director and CEO of the Oregon Hospice Association.

Another analysis concluded that these wider improvements in end-of-life care were a "silver lining" to the controversial law, delivering benefits even to those who may have opposed it.[10]

Opponents of aid-in-dying frequently warn that it creates a "slippery slope" toward involuntary euthanasia and the targeting of vulnerable populations—people who are elderly, disabled, poor, racial or ethnic minorities, mentally ill, uninsured, or uneducated. To date, however, no evidence of abuse or misuse of the law has occurred.[11] Physicians decline twenty-four of every twenty-five aid-in-dying requests, indicating that questionable cases (those with mental health impairments) are screened out of the process early on.[12] Anyone who is physically incapacitated but not terminally ill cannot use the law. Participation is entirely voluntary, for the patients as well as for physicians. Guardians or medical proxies cannot attempt to invoke the law on behalf of another person. Only five percent of Oregon's 2018 Death with Dignity patients reported that the cost of continuing their treatment was a concern.

---

7. http://lists.opn.org/pipermail/right-to-die_lists.opn.org/2005-March/000730.html.
8. http://www.willamette.edu/law/resources/journals/review/pdf/Volume%2045/WLR45-1_Jackson_11_18_08.pdf.
9. http://www.ncbi.nlm.nih.gov/pubmed/26172615.
10. M. Lee and S. Tolle. "The Silver Lining," *Archives of Internal Medicine*. January 15, 1996, p.267-269.
11. http://jme.bmj.com/content/37/3/171.abstract.
12. http://onlinelibrary.wiley.com/doi/10.1111/nyas.12486/abstract.

While some disability rights advocates vehemently oppose medical aid-in-dying laws,[13] many disabled voters feel differently. In Connecticut, 65% of those voters supported such laws;[14] in Massachusetts, 74%;[15] and in New Jersey, 63%,[16] according to polls done in 2014. An editor for *New Mobility* magazine, a disability-rights publication, said that its readership is split on the issue of aid-in-dying, with about half supporting it and half against it.[17] A few groups like the Disability Rights Legal Center[18] and the Utah Chapter of the Legislative Coalition for People with Disabilities actually support medical aid-in-dying.[19]

Much of the opposition to aid-in-dying comes from those who cite religious or moral grounds. Most faiths have prohibitions against the practice. Indeed, the most vocal and well-funded opponent is the US Conference of Catholic Bishops. Yet polling on the issue in New York state from 2015 showed strong support among faith believers: 74% of Catholics, 74% of Protestants, and 83% of Jews support aid-in-dying.[20] Among faith believers, only one subgroup consistently opposed the concept—those who attend religious services more than once a week. This issue has parallels to contraception, where the Catholic Church hierarchy is out of touch with congregants, the vast majority of whom do not follow church doctrine on that question.[21]

The medical profession has been another source of resistance to aid-in-dying laws. The American Medical Association, with nearly a quarter-million members and a multi-million dollar lobbying budget, still officially opposes them, saying "it is fundamentally incompatible

---

13. http://notdeadyet.org/assisted-suicide-talking-points.

14. https://drive.google.com/a/compassionandchoices.org/file/d/0B3IuDjCAxxv7bF9ETDgzS1B2RmJ1aWdMUGRqeHJibVdIUWI0/view?pref=2&pli=1.

15. https://drive.google.com/file/d/0B3IuDjCAxxv7eXdPUXJtTEtYc0NZNFFoSDJWYkNvTlM4aWk0/view?pref=2&pli=1.

16. http://www.compassionandchoices.org/userfiles/New-Jersey-Purple-Poll-Memo-February-2014.pdf.

17. http://www.witf.org/smart-talk/2014/12/smart-talk-dying-with-dignity-laws-in-pa.php.

18. https://disabilityrightslegalcenter.org/end-life-liberty-project.

19. https://www.compassionandchoices.org/utah-disabilities-group-endorses-aid-in-dying-legislation/.

20. Eagle Point Strategies, LLC, New York Statewide Survey September 2015, 1000 registered New York voters.

21. https://www.reuters.com/article/us-most-catholic-women-us-use-birth-cont-idUSTRE73D4SZ20110414.

with the physician's role as healer."[22] However, there have always been doctors who recognize that some dying patients suffer greatly and may wish to hasten their inevitable deaths. As far back as 1906, some physicians supported bills in Ohio and Iowa that would have allowed them to administer the anesthetic chloroform until a peaceful death occurred.[23] They felt it was important for them to regulate a practice that at that time was frequent and widely-used.[24] But those early legislative proposals drew strong opposition and never came close to passing.

Public support for medical aid-in-dying has increased significantly since Oregon began allowing it in 1997. As of mid-2019, the practice was authorized in eight more states—Washington, Montana, Vermont, California, Colorado, Hawaii, New Jersey, and Maine—plus the District of Columbia. The legalization effort gained new momentum in 2014, with Brittany Maynard's courageous and well-publicized decision to move to Oregon so that she could die at age twenty-nine, rather than wait for a virulent type of brain cancer to incapacitate and eventually kill her. California, where Maynard lived before moving to Oregon, legalized aid-in-dying in 2015. Colorado did so in 2016, the District of Columbia in 2017, Hawaii in 2018, and New Jersey and Maine in 2019.

National polls show that support for aid-in-dying laws is strong across the country. In a 2014 Harris poll, 74% of Americans were in favor.[25] Three years later, a Gallup poll found similarly strong support, with 67% approving the idea.[26]

Support from the medical profession is growing, too. A clear majority of physicians—57%—now favor aid-in-dying legislation, up from 46% in 2010.[27] Several state medical societies, including those in California, Colorado, Connecticut, District of Columbia, Maine, Maryland,

22. https://www.ama-assn.org/delivering-care/physician-assisted-suicide.
23. Giza Lopes. *Dying with Dignity: A Legal Approach to Assisted Death*. Praeger, 2015, pp. 20-23.
24. Giza Lopes. *Dying with Dignity: A Legal Approach to Assisted Death*. Praeger, 2015, p. 36.
25. http://www.theharrispoll.com/health-and-life/Most_Americans_Agree_With_Right-to-Die_Movement.html.
26. http://news.gallup.com/poll/211928/majority-americans-remain-supportive-euthanasia.aspx.
27. https://www.medscape.com/viewarticle/873844.

Massachusetts, Minnesota, Nevada, New Mexico, Oregon, and Vermont, have dropped their opposition and now take a neutral stance. Overall, neurologists, who treat patients with devastating degenerative diseases like as ALS, have also dropped their opposition. In February 2018, their professional association, the American Academy of Neurology, voted to allow its members to follow their own judgment on the question.[28] Some medical groups have gone further and declared their support for aid-in-dying, including the American Public Health Association, the American Medical Student Association, the American Women's Medical Association, the American College of Legal Medicine, and the New York State Academy of Family Physicians.[29]

However, when the necessary legislation is proposed at the state level, elected officials do not always heed the overwhelming public support. Politically powerful groups like the Catholic Church and Right to Life can often block aid-in-dying bills because they have allies in key legislative positions. Legislators who support aid-in-dying may be reluctant to take on such powerful political adversaries. And the mixed messages from the medical profession can give skittish legislators a convenient reason to put the issue aside. After Brittany Maynard's life-ending decision drew so much national attention, aid-in-dying bills were introduced in more than half the states in America, but only in California, Hawaii, New Jersey, and Maine did legislators pass them into law.

The California aid-in-dying law was overturned on a procedural technicality in May 2018 by a California Superior Court judge, after opponents of the law filed a lawsuit. The opponents—the Life Legal Defense Foundation, and the American Academy of Medical Ethics—are antiabortion organizations that oppose aid-in-dying. The American Academy of Medical Ethics also preaches abstinence before marriage, claims homosexual behaviors are destructive and burdensome to society, and say the practice of medicine involves covenants with a Deity.[30]

28. http://n.neurology.org/content/neurology/90/9/420.full.pdf.

29. https://www.compassionandchoices.org/wp-content/uploads/2018/03/FS-Medical-Professional-Associations-that-Recognize-Medical-Aid-in-Dying-3.02.18-1.pdf.

30. http://ethicalhealthcare.org/About/Our-Mission-Vision.

The California 4th District Circuit of Appeal Court, on June 15, 2018, suspended the Superior Court ruling, allowing aid-in-dying patients in the state to continue to access the law while it worked its way through the appeals process. On February 27, 2019, in a clear victory for supporters of aid-in-dying, the California Supreme Court rejected the opponents' appeal to invalidate the law. As of this writing, the case will return to Riverside County District Court, where opponents have vowed to continue their efforts to overturn the law.

In Colorado, when the legislature refused to act, citizens gathered the necessary signatures and put the issue to a statewide vote. As in other states, the majority of funding to fight the ballot initiative came from the Catholic church.[31] Supporter Bart Windrum, of Boulder, complained that opponents of aid-in-dying were fighting that effort by citizens instead of "acting positively to promote the medical reforms that they subscribe to and that they rightfully say will benefit everybody."[32] Despite the bitter and well-funded opposition, Colorado voters passed Proposition 106, the End of Life Options, in November 2016 by nearly a 2-1 margin.[33]

In late 2016, the District of Columbia Council passed its own aid-in-dying law by an 11-2 vote. This law, which went through the local government's full legislative process, including extensive hearings, drew attacks from religious conservatives. They asked US Congress to use its veto authority over DC government decisions and kill the aid-in-dying law.[34] After that tactic failed, congressional opponents attempted to deny DC the funding for the upgraded electronic medical filing system needed to make the new law work. Politicians elected by voters from elsewhere in the country were not only attacking District of Columbia residents' right to self-government, they were attacking the right of individuals to determine their own fate at the end of life. As DC Council member Mary Cheh, who introduced the bill, said at the time, "This is about

31. http://www.coloradoindependent.com/161839/ballot-measure-spending-hits-a-high-watermark.

32. http://www.dailycamera.com/guest-opinions/ci_30539831/bart-windrum-end-life-options-act-small-medical.

33. http://www.denverpost.com/2016/11/08/colorado-aid-in-dying-proposition-106-election-results/.

34. https://www.washingtonpost.com/opinions/dc-defied-a-responsibility-of-governing-in-passing-its-death-with-dignity-act/2017/01/27/693c74a6-e256-11e6-a547-5fb9411d332c_story.html?utm_term=.c0b5f988eace.

the people of the District of Columbia, and whether they can have any control over their own lives."[35]

I support aid-in-dying; I believe my father would have supported it too. Seeing how end-of-life care evolved in Oregon after Death with Dignity was enacted, I have to believe that such a law in Pennsylvania would have made a tremendous difference for my father, regardless of whether he actually decided to use the option. As in Oregon, Pennsylvania's doctors and hospitals would have been prompted to improve comfort care for those facing the end of life. Perhaps the Hospice of Central Pennsylvania would not have been so callously indifferent to my father's repeated complaints about pain. With better hospice care and a prescription for life-ending medication in hand, Dad may have never felt the need to use it, as is the case for a full third of people who obtain life-ending prescriptions. Another big advantage of jurisdictions with aid-in-dying is that they make a legal distinction between the desire of the dying to have a comfortable and peaceful end on their own terms versus a mental health crisis that leads to suicide.

I appreciate that some people have moral, religious, and philosophical objections to aid-in-dying. However, those who object to it—patients or doctors—are not required to participate in it. Mentally competent adults should have the liberty to make the important decisions about their lives, especially at the end of life, without the shackle of laws imposed by powerful political minorities who want to dictate the intensely personal choices that others make. I hope those who oppose aid-in-dying will cease their efforts to impose their will on people who support it. As legislators in California came to realize after they saw the terrible choice Brittany Maynard had to make, no terminally ill person should have to move to another state to be able to decide how and when their life will end.

35. http://wamu.org/story/17/05/23/trump-budget-aims-block-funding-d-c-death-dignity-law/.

CHAPTER 16

A Path Forward from Heartache

Once the storm is over you won't remember how you made it through, how you managed to survive. You won't even be sure, in fact, whether the storm is really over. But one thing is certain. When you come out of the storm you won't be the same person who walked in.

—Haruki Murakami, *Kafka On the Shore*

WHEN I WALKED out of the front door of my parents' home on February 7, 2013, under arrest and flanked by police officers, my life as I knew it had vanished. There was no advance warning of what I was about to face; nothing in life prepared me for the traumas my family and I were about to endure. My life became one filled with anguish, foreboding, and overwhelming darkness, with only flickering moments of relief.

The powerful forces that threw my life into turmoil still exist. Our health-care systems remain focused on extending life. Even those who, like my father, prepare carefully in advance, run the risk of dying in a futile cascade of invasive, sometimes brutal, and completely unwanted medical treatment. Those who care for a loved one who is ready to die must tread carefully, lest they do something that someone believes should be investigated. Should the police become involved, your innocence is not enough to protect you. Those who are blissfully ignorant and unsuspecting of all this could find themselves in the same situation I did. And that is why I feel compelled to speak out.

I have spoken about my experience to more than a hundred audiences, large and small, professional and community-based, educator and student, faith-based and secular. None were more daunting than my talk in October 2015 to the Business and Professional Women's Club in Pottsville, Pennsylvania, my personal ground zero. I'd hesitated to accept the invitation. On each visit back to where my father lived and died, traumatic moments would flood back to me. But I felt that I needed to find the courage to do it. And I told myself that the handful of people responsible for how I was treated in Pottsville does not represent the entire community.

So, I walked into the room prepared to tell my story. Having given so many talks, I knew what I would say, and I'd always drawn overwhelmingly supportive reactions. Yet I had an uneasy feeling in my stomach.

I was greeted warmly by the group's vice president, who then introduced me to several of the members. As I moved across the room, to my surprise and shock, I noticed Coroner Moylan's congressional campaign manager, who was there as an invited guest of a member, a few feet from me. Immediately, my heart skipped and fluttered, and I felt every erratic beat. As the palpitations continued, I wondered if I'd had a lapse in judgment in agreeing to speak here. Would this be a hostile audience?

Blocking out my doubts, I stood at the lectern and began my talk. As usual, I mentioned the role of Coroner Moylan, and how experts rejected his bizarre conclusions about my father's death. I mentioned that Moylan went on to run for Congress on a platform extolling the "sanctity of life," with my father's case as an example. As I did so, I looked his campaign manager right in the eye. She held my gaze. She was neither hostile nor empathetic, but she didn't look away.

As I continued explaining what happened to me and my father, I could feel how the audience grew appalled as it learned about the suffering inflicted on both of us. When I finished, I received a standing ovation. A couple days later, I learned that a long-time member reported that it was the only standing ovation she remembered in her thirty years with the group. Their reactions speak to the deep well of anxiety in our culture about the medically intensive, impersonal, invasive way so many of us are going to die. People would rather not think about it, but when they do, as caregivers, they don't want to fear being second-guessed by police and prosecutors for the care they give to their dying loved ones; as receivers of end-of-life care, they do not want to suffer like my father did.

In November 2015, I traveled to the Veterans Administration Medical Center in Miami, Florida, where I was the featured speaker at the professional training session known in the medical world as Special Grand Rounds. The VA had decided that talking about my family's agonizing end-of-life experience would help its staff throughout the region deliver more compassionate care that respects the wishes of dying patients. I was especially honored to speak in a hospital serving veterans. My father was proud of his military service, and over the years he continued to keep in touch with his army buddies through reunions of the 293rd MM Ordnance unit.

My presentation attracted triple the usual attendance and was broadcast to all the VA hospitals throughout Florida and south Georgia. As I stood at the lectern and gazed out at the auditorium full of medical professionals in their white coats, ready to tell Dad's story in a place that cares for veterans, I felt as if he were standing with me, smiling and pleased.

When I finished speaking, the hall filled with resounding applause. One of the organizers presented me with a small American flag in honor of Dad and his military service. Afterward, I couldn't even begin to count how many people lined up to express their sympathy and thanks for speaking. To a person, they wanted to avoid what happened to my father and were appalled at what happened to me. Every time I look at that American flag, now displayed on a shelf in my home, next to a picture of me and Dad at my wedding, I feel reassured that I did the right thing by my father and have honored his legacy by speaking out.

End-of-life care and options are a crucial and urgent element of my story. But equally pressing is letting audiences full of law-abiding citizens know what it is like to be victimized by the criminal justice system. I have been told by prosecutors I've met in various cities—New York City, Pittsburgh, Houston, San Diego—that they would never have prosecuted a case like mine. I discovered errors and bad practices at all levels of the criminal justice system. I was probably only able to extricate myself from the fearsome machinery of injustice because I was middle-class, white, had a competent defense lawyer who worked diligently for me—and because I was lucky enough to have my case land before a judge to whom truth and justice mattered.

The people who had a hand in this did not come away unscathed. The clinical director of Hospice of Central Pennsylvania, Barbara Woods, retired just after my preliminary hearing. Pottsville police captain Steven Durkin retired soon after my case was dismissed. Hospice of Central Pennsylvania was publicly criticized in news reports and on television. Schuylkill County district attorney Karen Byrnes-Noon lost her election months after she handed my case to the Pennsylvania attorney general's office. Pennsylvania attorney general Kathleen Kane was herself prosecuted and convicted in a case unrelated to mine. Schuylkill County coroner David Moylan lost in his bid for US Congress, but he was re-elected coroner in 2015. I don't know whether hospice nurse Barbara Cattermole or hospice team leader Deborah Hornberger still work for Hospice of Central Pennsylvania. As of late 2018, senior deputy attorney general Anthony Forray, whom Judge Russell thoroughly criticized in her opinion, was still working as a prosecutor for the Pennsylvania attorney general's office, now headed by Attorney General Josh Shapiro.

Though I won my court case, the unfortunate reality is that we all lost in some way. The case wasted taxpayer money and diverted time and money from pursuing more valid and urgent criminal cases. It instilled fear in people who are dying and those who care for them. It eroded public trust in hospice providers. It gave law-abiding citizens good reason to question their confidence in our criminal justice system.

I narrowly escaped the socially destructive cycle of arrests, prosecutions, and plea-bargained convictions that has given our country the world's largest prison population. Like most people, I want to live in a safe society. But to be truly safe, we need a fair and equitable justice system, one that is less focused on winning convictions and more focused on making sure that the right people are charged and prosecuted, and that, if justly convicted, they serve sentences appropriate to their crimes.

I'm often asked if I have sued the police, prosecutors, or hospice for the suffering they inflicted on my family and me. The answer is no. Prosecutors have absolute immunity from lawsuits. Police have what's known as "qualified immunity," which makes it very difficult to win a lawsuit when they engage in misconduct. Any suit against the hospice for its failures in caring for my dad would have to be filed by my mother, as she is his next of kin. However, my attorney advised that pursuing the case would take four or five years, and my mother would subject herself to what would surely be a stressful, emotionally wrenching process, including a potentially hostile deposition conducted by lawyers for the hospice. That would have been too much for Mom—she can't even bear to sit through another viewing of the *60 Minutes* broadcast about our ordeal. Going through several more years of legal battles, with an uncertain outcome, simply wasn't worth the agony it would inflict on her.

After the painful, futile, almost abusive medical treatment imposed on my father, and the injustice inflicted on me, I found the courage to speak out. I found the strength to fight back against an unjust criminal justice system, and I have become much more aware of how that system abuses those who do not have the advantages I had. I completed paralegal studies, did an internship with the Pennsylvania Innocence Project, and in 2018 I began work as a pre-trial assistant for the Montgomery County Office of the Public Defender, where much of my work time is spent interviewing indigent clients at the county jail. In a remarkable and ironic twist to my story, this is the very jail where former Pennsylvania attorney general Kathleen Kane, who pursued *my* prosecution, served her eight-month sentence.

My faith in humanity was renewed by the many people who reached out to offer support and encouragement. My husband stood resolutely by me, as did the rest of my family. I have been inspired by and have learned from the many people I have encountered.

I have found my path forward.

Along the way, I drew inspiration, as did many others, from Brittany Maynard and her courageous, highly public decision to end her life at age twenty-nine because brain cancer had ravaged her body with unbearable headaches, seizures, and vomiting, and would soon render her blind and unable to speak. I regret that I was never able to meet Brittany. I did write her a letter, and to my great astonishment, she responded just before she died.

> *Dear Barbara,*
>
> *It meant so much for me to receive your kind letter the other day, especially as I am preparing for my own passing. I am familiar with the history of your case and have always been appalled that it was ever litigated. I am so sorry you had to endure that. It is clear to me, in my heart, that you were doing your very best to care for your terminally ailing father. That is a difficult job. As a terminally ill person myself, I understand what that level of sacrifice means for a loving and supportive family on an emotional, physical, and financial level.*
>
> *It has comforted me to see your work and the power of your story. It resonates with Americans. Stories like yours and mine put human faces on a controversial topic that many politicians are happy to sweep under the rug.*
>
> *I had the pleasure of speaking with Governor Jerry Brown the other day regarding this issue. While he was not exactly jumping up and down to advocate for aid-in-dying at this moment, it was clear that he supported my personal decision when my illness was explained to him. He was genuinely interested in my personal story and the impact on the California community. That is usually my experience, that when people are brought to understand the humanity of suffering in a terminal illness, when they understand what*

aid-in-dying as an end-of-life CHOICE offers, it is hard for them to reason against it.

I am truly proud to have been able to make a positive contribution to this imperative healthcare movement. All Americans deserve access to the same healthcare rights. I wish I could have had the pleasure of meeting you in person, but this letter will have to do. I hope you continue to powerfully speak out on behalf of the terminally ill and our right to access the choice of dignity in death.

—Warm regards, Brittany Maynard[1]

Yes, Brittany, I continued to speak out—and I will.

1. Brittany Maynard, email to author, 11/1/2014.

APPENDIX A

Advance Directives

The best way to get the care you want at the end of life is to discuss your wishes in advance with loved ones and your health-care provider(s) and to put your instructions in legally enforceable documents. Here are important things to know about the process, with references for getting more specific guidance.

An ADVANCE DIRECTIVE is a document you prepare in case you are incapacitated and can't make your own health-care decisions. The directive explains the medical treatments you want (or don't want). It is also known as a "living will."

You should also prepare a document designating someone who has the legal power to carry out the wishes expressed in your advance directive. That person is your HEALTH-CARE PROXY, also known as a DURABLE POWER OF ATTORNEY, for making your health-care decisions.

To prepare these documents, you do not need an attorney. Sample forms are available for your state on the internet, and the one for your advance directive usually includes a health-care proxy section.

However, these generic state forms are often vaguely worded and cover just a few extreme medical conditions. I highly recommend consulting an attorney who has experience in advising clients about end-of-life issues.

Everyone age eighteen and older should have an advance directive and designate someone as a health-care proxy. Tragic events can strike at any age. If you are incapacitated and want to refuse life-prolonging treatment, federal and state court rulings require clear and convincing evidence that you wish to do so.

Preparing these documents can help prevent you from being subject to invasive and likely futile treatment intended to delay death at all costs. Advance directives can also specify which lifesaving measures you wish to have done. Here are the key steps involved. However, as my father's case shows, having these written documents does not guarantee that your wishes will be honored, especially in emergency situations outside a hospital.

Preparing Your Advance Directive

It's more than just a fill-in-the-blanks process

⌘ Understand What is Most Important to You

A good way to start is by asking yourself "If I had a medical crisis or were on the verge of dying, what do I want people to know about me, and what would I tell them to do for me?"

Consider questions like:

- Do I want to let nature take its course, or do I want every possible thing done to extend my life?
- Is the quality of life I'll have after treatment important or irrelevant?
- Do I want as much relief as possible from pain, even if it means I may die sooner?
- How important is it for me to remain mentally alert and physically capable?
- Is leaving a good impression on my loved ones—how I want them to remember me in my last moments—a major concern?
- How important is it to die at home instead of a hospital?
- Do I want to donate my organs?

Compassion and Choices, the organization that helped me after my father's death, has a worksheet that is helpful for this stage, when you are reflecting on your values.[1]

THINK AHEAD TO THE KINDS OF MEDICAL PROCEDURES YOU WANT (AND DON'T WANT)

You'll need to consider some of the most common treatment decisions that arise in life-threatening or end-of-life situations.

Would you want to be kept alive indefinitely, with no hope of recovery, through use of a respirator?

What if you had to spend the rest of your life bedridden, living only because you are hooked up to tubes that deliver your food and water? (In that circumstance, it is legal for you to refuse food and/or water, a process known as VOLUNTARY STOPPING EATING AND DRINKING.)

If you are already near death in a hospital, and your heart or breathing stops, would you want to refuse CPR or electroshocks to your heart? (If so, you would need a DO NOT RESUSCITATE ORDER, or DNR.)

Infections like pneumonia often cause the death of frail, elderly patients who are hospitalized for other conditions. Hospitals routinely go all out to fight those infections, even if it merely delays death by a few days or weeks. You may choose to decline that treatment.

When you are in the hospital and key organs—heart or kidneys—begin to fail, hospitals by default will take heroic measures to sustain them, regardless of how long it might help you live. If death is likely to come soon anyway, would you want to refuse that treatment? When considering intensive hospital treatments routinely used at the end of life, an option is to instruct your doctors to try them first, but if they fail to work, then discontinue them. Compassion and Choices has a helpful checklist to guide your decisions on these questions.[2]

---

1. https://www.compassionandchoices.org/wp-content/uploads/2016/03/Values_Worksheet.pdf.
2. https://www.compassionandchoices.org/wp-content/uploads/2016/03/My_Particular_Wishes.pdf.

⌘ Decide Whom You Can Trust to Exercise Your Health-care Proxy

Appointing your health-care proxy is the most important decision you will make. You should select *one* person, although you can authorize one or two others as back-up proxies. The person(s) you pick must agree in advance to be your proxy.

In selecting someone, consider whether your proxy:

- ✦ Will be committed to carrying out your wishes, whether or not he/she agrees with them;
- ✦ Can serve as your advocate in dealing with doctors and other authority figures during stressful situations;
- ✦ Can resist pressure from others who may not agree with your wishes.

⌘ Talk to Your Loved Ones and Your Doctors

Your first task is to speak with the person you hope will serve as your health-care proxy and make sure he or she is comfortable doing so. You can choose to give your health-care proxy the authority to depart from the instructions in your advance directive and decide on his or her own about what's best for you. Obviously, you'd have to have total confidence in that person's judgment.

Talking with other loved ones is important, too—especially if some hold different values that might cause conflict when your proxy follows through with your instructions.

It can be hard to broach the subject of death, especially if you wait until it's clear the end of life is coming soon. It's much easier to talk about the subject when you are healthy.

Don't rely on doctors to bring up end-of-life planning, especially if you are in poor health but do not have a terminal diagnosis. Most doctors agree these conversations are important, but talking about death is awkward and difficult. Few doctors have training on how to bring the subject up in a way that feels comfortable.[3]

---

3. Seventy-five percent of physicians believe they are responsible for initiating end-of-life conversations, yet only 29% have had formal training in end-of-life talks, and almost half feel unsure what to say. https://www.johnahartford.org/newsroom/view/advance-care-planning-poll.

For advice on how to start these conversations, the Institute of Medicine has a good list of resources.[4] The Conversation Project's guide[5] is particularly helpful.

PREPARE DOCUMENTS

Several websites have sample forms for preparing an advance directive and health-care proxy. The relevant form varies from state to state. AARP's site has a guide to forms for all fifty states.[6]

Typically, you'll need the signature of two witnesses. The forms don't have to be notarized, but if you travel frequently out of your home state, notarizing the directive and proxy will improve the odds your instructions will be honored in other states.

Again, I do advise consulting an attorney with experience in this field. But starting the process by checking out the online forms is a good way to prepare for getting more detailed legal guidance.

Additional Options: Orders to Be Signed by a Physician

DNR (DO NOT RESUSCITATE)

The DNR is a binding medical order signed by a physician. If your heart stops beating and you stop breathing, it directs health-care providers to refrain from giving you CPR (chest compressions and artificial ventilation) or electroshocks to restart your heart.

It is an option for people who know they are near the end of life—frail, elderly patients; and those who are terminally ill or slowly dying of chronic diseases like COPD or congestive heart failure. A DNR is most commonly used when the end-of-life patient is getting care for other conditions in a hospital. However, it is also available to those who are still at home, in assisted living, or in a nursing home. It is not a do-it-yourself form—it is an official medical order that must be signed by a physician,

4. http://www.nationalacademies.org/hmd/Reports/2014/Dying-In-America-Improving-Quality-and-Honoring-Individual-Preferences-Near-the-End-of-Life/The-Conversation.aspx.
5. https://theconversationproject.org/.
6. https://www.aarp.org/caregiving/financial-legal/free-printable-advance-directives/.

and so must be prepared in advance, while you can still make that decision for yourself. (Or, you can direct your health-care proxy to discuss a DNR with the physician in the event you lose decisional capacity and further treatment is futile.)

In emergency situations in some jurisdictions, an advance directive may be enough to prevent medics from performing unwanted CPR. Having a physician write an out-of-hospital DNR offers extra insurance that you will not undergo treatment you do not want.

POLST (Physician Order for Life-Sustaining Treatment)

A POLST is designed for persons of *any age* with a serious illness or life-limiting illness. It allows patients, working with their physicians, to determine in advance of a medical crisis which treatments they will allow or refuse, or use for a trial period. It must be signed by a doctor or qualified health-care provider, not an attorney. In states that have adopted it, all health-care personnel are expected to honor it, including emergency medical services.[7]

POLST forms are usually brightly colored paper. Copies are not usually accepted, so the original form needs to accompany patients wherever they go.

Distribute Documents

All your advance planning will go for naught if the documents cannot be found when needed. Make copies of your advance directive and health-care proxy and distribute them to the person who will make your medical decisions, your loved ones, your doctor(s), and your hospital. If you are in hospice care, assisted living, or a nursing home, make sure your records on file there include your directives.

A note of caution: This last stage—ensuring your instructions are known and acted upon—is where things are most likely to go wrong. As soon as it appears that your life is threatened in any way, the medical system is primed to kick into life-saving mode and begin delivering

7. http://polst.org/about/.

intensive treatment. To ward off unwanted care, your documents need to be known in advance or readily accessible.

One option is to pay to store them with an internet-based service, such as Living Will Registry.[8] However, in an emergency, hospital staff seldom take the time to check for patient information in the cloud or outside their system. They may try looking once, and if they don't find anything or can't access the document, they won't try again.

Your local health-care provider may put your directives in its electronic record system, and that can be helpful. However, your provider's record system may not make it very easy to find your instructions. An ethicist from one health-care system told me that its electronic system stores advance directives under a separate tab, marked "Miscellaneous," which is almost never opened.

Some people carry their advance directives around on a flash drive, but many hospitals will not try to read them, from fear of introducing computer viruses. Health-care providers are much more likely to notice a hard copy or a DNR bracelet than to go looking into a person's wallet to find information about an advance directive.

The best advice is to keep your own copies in an *easily accessible* place. Many people post their health-care documents and medicine lists on the refrigerator. This is the first place emergency medical responders will look if they are called into your home.

The take-home message: The more widely you discuss and share your advance planning documents, the better.

Regularly Review and Update Your Instructions

This step is especially important if you have prepared your directives when you are in full health, and then experience a dramatic change in your circumstances. (Potentially significant changes are not limited to medical conditions. Divorce, estrangement from family members, or new personal beliefs can affect your plans as well.)

8. http://www.uslivingwillregistry.com/.

Getting the care you want in a medical crisis, especially at the end of life, is a *not* a set-it-and-forget-it process. It takes regular communication with your loved ones and health-care providers so they know what you want. What you want can change over time, so make sure your written documents are updated as needed.

RESOURCES FOR END-OF-LIFE CONVERSATIONS AND ADVANCE-CARE PLANNING:

- Institute of Medicine's "Conversation Resources": http://www.nationalacademies.org/hmd/Reports/2014/Dying-In-America-Improving-Quality-and-Honoring-Individual-Preferences-Near-the-End-of-Life/The-Conversation.aspx
- Compassion and Choices: compassionandchoices.org
  - The group offers an end-of-life toolkit and other helpful resources, including a dementia provision: https://www.compassionandchoices.org/eolc/
- PREPARE: prepareyourcare.org
- The Conversation Project: theconversationproject.org
- National Healthcare Decisions Day: https://www.nhdd.org/about/#about-us
- Dementia-specific advance directive developed by Dr. Barak Gaster[9]: https://static1.squarespace.com/static/5a0128cf8fd4d22ca11a405d/t/5ab55969562fa77d1761c62a/1521834345937/dementia-directive.pdf

9. https://www.nytimes.com/2018/01/19/health/dementia-advance-directive.html.

APPENDIX B

Choosing a Hospice

When my father agreed to get hospice care, there are many things I wish I'd known. Here are some of the important points that would have helped us make a more informed choice about hospice care. This appendix also includes recommendations for questions you should ask when considering a hospice, plus a list of helpful resources.

- Hospice care is now a multi-billion-dollar industry, where the push for profits can compromise care for patients. Experts in the industry agree that the quality of hospice care varies a great deal.
- You are free to pick the hospice you want (assuming there is more than one serving your area). Your doctor may recommend or refer you to a hospice, but you should *not* automatically choose it without further checking.
- Hospices are supposed to do more than simply ensure the patient's physical comfort. They are supposed to address a patient's emotional, social, and spiritual needs.
- Hospices are supposed to provide emotional, social, and spiritual support for the patient's caregivers as well as the patient.
- An interdisciplinary team is supposed to be involved in caring for the hospice patient. By law, the team must include a physician, registered nurse, social worker, and spiritual counselor; it may also include home health aides and trained volunteers.

- Each hospice patient is supposed to have an individual care plan. You need to be involved in preparing the plan and make sure it fits your loved one's situation. (In my father's case, the hospice never discussed his care plan with us, and they failed to inform us of the medicines that were ordered for his symptom control.)
- You can choose to have your doctor continue as the "attending medical professional" who supervises your hospice care, or you can let a hospice doctor take over. All the services provided for the care of the terminal illness are the hospice's responsibility. The hospice must coordinate your care with your doctor if he/she continues as the primary physician.
- If your hospice care is covered by Medicare, the hospice gets paid a fixed amount for every day you are enrolled, regardless of whether you receive any services that day. This creates a strong financial incentive to scrimp on the services you get. It helps explain why the quality of care can vary greatly among hospices.
- Almost two-thirds of hospices are now for-profit corporations, and they average about fourteen dollars of profit on every hundred dollars they charge for serving Medicare patients. There are good for-profit hospices and bad non-profit hospices, but on balance, non-profits deliver more services at less cost. That's because hospice care is a labor-intensive business. Profit-driven hospices have more incentive to be as efficient as possible, but they don't have many opportunities to replace human workers with labor-saving technology or innovative management that cut costs.
- Hospice services are supposed to be available twenty-four hours a day, seven days a week, year-round. In reality, hospices have significantly less staff on duty outside of regular business hours, which can cause significant delays responding to patients who have urgent needs for medication or other assistance. (This is a serious problem in hospice care, according to Kaiser Health News[1] and the

1. https://khn.org/news/no-one-is-coming-hospice-patients-abandoned-at-deaths-door/.

US government's inspector general who oversees Medicare.[2])

- There are four levels of hospice care.[3]

  1. ROUTINE CARE is delivered where the patient lives—at home, in assisted living, or in a nursing home. This is the type of hospice care most patients will receive.
  2. CONTINUOUS HOME CARE is a more intensive level of services, delivered where the patients live, for those having unbearable pain, psychological distress, or other crises that can be treated at home instead of a hospital. The care, which can range from eight to twenty-four hours a day, will be led by a nurse, usually with help from hospice aides or the patient's caregivers. This level of care is permitted only for brief times of crisis.
  3. GENERAL INPATIENT CARE begins when other efforts to manage pain or other major medical symptoms have not worked. This more intensive and expensive level of care can be provided directly by the hospice, by a Medicare-certified hospital, or by a nursing facility that has a registered nursing service available to patients twenty-four hours a day. General inpatient care is intended to be short-term care.
  4. INPATIENT RESPITE CARE provides temporary relief to the patient's primary caregiver. It can be provided by the hospice, a hospital, or a long-term care facility that has enough round-the-clock nursing personnel to guarantee that patient's needs are met. Respite care is provided for no more than five consecutive days.

Most hospices offer the routine level of care. If you need the other three levels of service, a hospice may provide them directly or may contract with other providers to serve you.

2. https://www.npr.org/sections/health-shots/2018/07/31/634075540/hhs-inspector-generals-report-finds-flaws-and-fraud-in-u-s-hospice-care.

3. From the National Hospice and Palliative Care Association, https://www.nhpco.org/sites/default/files/public/Statistics_Research/Hospice_Levels_of_Care.pdf.

- If the person being considered for hospice care has dementia, proceed with caution. Dementia patients can be financially attractive to a hospice if they already live in supportive settings (assisted living or a nursing home). Those patients require little additional care from hospice personnel, making them a profitable addition to the hospice's patient list.
- Regardless of whether you live in an area that offers a choice of potential hospices, you should research the hospice and conduct an interview with its personnel before deciding to enroll yourself or a loved one.

Questions to Ask Before Selecting a Hospice

Here are some questions to guide your research into a hospice. The questions are drawn from the National Hospice and Palliative Care Organization (NHPCO)[4] and a helpful article in Journal of the American Medical Association (JAMA).[5] I have provided an abridged version of those questions and added some others. The list is fairly comprehensive, so select those questions most relevant to your personal circumstances.

The questions start with fairly basic criteria, which can be helpful in your initial screening, then move to more detailed questions you'd use when interviewing the hospice.

Beware of a hospice provider that is evasive or unwilling to answer your questions.

- Is the hospice Medicare certified?
- Is the hospice accredited by a national organization?[6] Ask if the hospice is a current NHPCO member, if it complies with NHPCO's Standards. (Note, however, that my father's hospice, Hospice of Central Pennsylvania, was Medicare-certified and

4. https://moments.nhpco.org/sites/default/files/public/moments/Choosing%20a%20Hospice.pdf.
5. http://jama.jamanetwork.com/article.aspx?articleid=183351.
6. http://moments.nhpco.org/sites/default/files/public/moments/Choosing%20a%20Hospice.pdf.

a member of NHPCO. Clearly, those two markers do not guarantee that patients receive high-quality care.)

- Are physicians and nurses certified in hospice and palliative care?
- Is there an interdisciplinary team (physicians, nurses, social workers, home health aides, spiritual counselors, volunteers) with appropriate training?
- Has the hospice been surveyed by a state or federal oversight agency in the last five years?
- What is the average caseload of each home care nurse? (For a full-time hospice nurse, a caseload of ten to twelve home hospice patients is ideal).
- How does the hospice ensure that service is available twenty-four hours a day, seven days a week? Is after-hours help available only by phone, or will the hospice send staff to the patient's home if needed? What is the backup plan if an on-duty nurse receives more than one urgent call for help? Are spiritual and social workers available outside of business hours? When a patient's hospice doctor is on vacation or off-duty, how does the hospice respond to requests for prescription renewals or other medical services?
- Does the hospice offer alternative therapies, such as massage, therapeutic touch, singing, or playing music?
- How does the hospice involve the patient and caregivers in preparing the patient's care plan? How often is that plan updated? How are the patient and caregivers involved in those updates?
- How are concerns about the opioid epidemic affecting the hospice's approach to relieving a patient's pain? How does the hospice ensure that patients obtain their desired level of comfort, especially when the patient is in home care and can self-administer pain medicine?
- How does the hospice ensure that it honors a patient's wishes in cases where an individual on staff may personally object to what the patient wants? Are there any circumstances in which the hospice would override a patient's advance directive?

- If you so desire, will the hospice allow the patient's primary doctor to continue directing the medical care?
- How is information about the patient shared among physicians on hospice staff and the patient's own doctors?
- Is there one case manager assigned to the patient? Who coordinates the care in different settings?
- Does the hospice provide the medications needed to control pain and other symptoms? Does the interdisciplinary team include a pharmacist to handle prescriptions?
- How many of its patients actually received more than just home-based hospice care? (Beware if the answer is zero. As a US government inspector general's report noted, when 100% of a hospice's patients receive nothing more than routine home care, it calls into question whether the patients are getting the more intensive services they might need to control pain and other symptoms, such as general inpatient care and continuous home care.)[7]
- What is the hospice's live discharge rate? (This measure is the percentage of patients who leave the hospice's care before death.) A high live discharge rate may reflect valid reasons—such as doctors sincerely misjudging patients' life expectancies. However, frequent live discharges may be a warning sign. Patients may leave at high rates because they (or loved ones) are unhappy with the care. The hospice may be aggressively enrolling patients who are not in fact terminally ill with six months or less to live. Profit-driven hospices have an incentive to do so because these patients do not cost a lot to serve but yield the same daily payment from Medicare as terminally ill patients. This is a distressingly common tactic some hospices have used to boost profits in some states.
- If the patient's caregiver(s) needs respite care, what is the process to request it? Does the hospice itself provide the respite care, or does it contract with another provider? Is there a waiting list?

---

7. https://oig.hhs.gov/oei/reports/oei-02-16-00570.pdf, at p. 5.

- If the patient has unrelieved pain or another medical crisis and needs hospital-style care, how does the hospice handle that? (That level of service, known as "general inpatient hospice care," is supposed to be available, either directly from the hospice or by contract with a hospital.) Does the hospice have a dedicated inpatient unit? How many beds are there? How long can a patient stay? Is there a waiting list to get in? Under what circumstances might the hospice send the patient to emergency care at a hospital?
- How does the hospice monitor and improve its quality of care?
- How many patient and caregiver complaints were received in the last year? How were they resolved?

Optional Questions About Palliative Sedation

Some patients heading into hospice may want their advance directive to authorize palliative sedation. (That's when a dying person has chosen to be sedated into unconsciousness, refusing all food and water, until death. It is legal in all fifty states.)

In that case:

- Ask the hospice whether it provides palliative sedation directly or if it refers patients to another provider.
- Does the hospice have any religious or ethical objection to helping patients obtain palliative sedation? (This is especially important when the hospice has a religious affiliation.)
- Does the hospice employ anyone who refuses on religious grounds to participate in palliative sedation? If so, how does the hospice arrange for the patient's advance directive to be honored?

Hospice Compare: A Useful Resource

Finally, another way to check out a hospice is the US government's Hospice Compare website.[8] Created by the Centers for Medicare and Medicaid Services (CMS), it has two kinds of information. One is self-reported information from the hospice, covering seven quality measures. The other is drawn from consumer feedback, based on surveys of family and friends of a patient who died under hospice care.

The site does not have any information about complaints filed against hospices or how valid those complaints might be.[9] Hospice Compare simply provides a "snapshot" of the quality of care. It should not be the sole basis for making your decision.

What Can You Do If You Are Unhappy with a Hospice?

If a hospice is not meeting your needs, there are several steps you can take:

- Complain, orally and/or in writing, to the administrator or ethics committee of the hospice
- File a report with your state Department of Health
- File a report with the US Center for Medicare and Medicaid Services
- Terminate the hospice and enroll in a different one.

I recommend trying to work out the problem with the hospice if your overall experience is acceptable, or if a problem seems to be with a particular employee. Whatever decision you make, the primary objective should be appropriate care for your dying loved one—care that honors his or her values, preferences, and wishes.

---

8. https://www.medicare.gov/hospicecompare/#about/about.
9. https://oig.hhs.gov/oei/reports/oei-02-16-00570.pdf, p.7.

Helpful Resources

- Patient website of the American Academy of Hospice and Palliative Medicine: http://palliativedoctors.org
- National Hospice and Palliative Care Organization: https://www.nhpco.org/quality/10-components-quality-care
- Hospice complaints: http://www.hospicepatients.org/stadrss.html
- Medicare hospice benefit booklet: http://www.medicare.gov/Pubs/pdf/02154.pdf
- Medicare complaints: http://www.patientsafetyasap.org/pdf/Medicare%20Complaints.pdf
- Hospice Compare: https://www.medicare.gov/hospicecompare/#about/about

APPENDIX C

End-of-Life Pain Management

Early in my father's enrollment in hospice I felt that his pain was not being properly addressed, although a fundamental principle of hospice care is to manage pain to allow for a comfortable death. I eventually learned there is an enormous difference between what proper end-of-life pain management looks like and what my father received from the hospice.

My purpose in discussing this topic is to make readers aware of what proper end-of-life pain management may entail; I do not intend to produce a comprehensive guide to pain management; some sources are listed for readers wanting more detailed information.

Effective pain management begins with a thorough assessment to identify the type of pain, its characteristics, and its intensity. Pain can arise from different sources depending on the underlying terminal condition, and there may be preexisting pain from previous chronic illness. Distinguishing the origin and type of pain is the bedrock of pain management. For example, cancer pain can feel very different from neuropathy pain (from damaged nerves) experienced by diabetics. However, the *principles* of managing pain apply to all of its sources:

1. The choice of pain medicine should be based on the type of pain. For example, neuropathy pain can be treated more effectively with methadone rather than morphine, and antidepressant medicines also help relieve this type of pain.[1] Anti-inflammatory

1. Quill, et al. *Primer of Palliative Care,* 6th ed., 2014, p.25.

drugs are helpful with somatic pain, a localized pain that can arise from tumors or arthritis.

2. People with chronic or frequently occurring pain should receive medications around the clock to avoid undertreated pain and to minimize side-effects. This maximizes their comfort and prevents unnecessary suffering.
3. Breakthrough pain (pain that occurs in-between regularly scheduled doses of pain medicine) should be treated with as-needed immediate-release pain relievers in addition to the regularly scheduled pain medicine. In general, as-needed-only prescribing should be avoided for people in persistent pain, as it will be difficult to achieve lasting pain control.
4. Pain medicine dosages should be adjusted promptly to allow effective pain relief. Undertreated pain is a significant end-of-life issue, and it can exact a terrible toll on the dying and their caregivers.[2]

In fact, the failure to recommend a long-acting opioid for round-the-clock pain management, along with an appropriate dose of a fast-acting (or immediate-release) opioid for breakthrough pain is a common error, one that can be avoided by including pharmacists in hospice care. Pharmacists can play an important counseling and educational role in hospice interdisciplinary team meetings. They assess the appropriateness of medication orders and ensure they are prescribed to provide effective symptom control. They can educate the hospice team about how best to use analgesics and other medicines to allow the best possible quality of life for the dying person.[3] The law does not require pharmacists to be part of each team, but many hospices value their input and include them.

At the end of life, significant pain is common; unfortunately, it is often undertreated, and research shows addiction continues to be a major fear of patients, caregivers, and physicians. Morphine, an opioid, is the medicine

---

2. http://www.aafp.org/afp/2000/0201/p755.html.
3. http://www.medscape.org/viewarticle/550895.

of choice to treat end-of-life pain because it works well for many people, and its cost is relatively low.[4] Significantly, research also shows that the addiction rate in the severely ill is remarkably low.[5] Understandably, there is great concern in the United States about the epidemic of prescription opioid abuse that has resulted in addiction, led to heroin use, and caused untimely and devastating overdose fatalities. All opioids have the potential for abuse, but the risk of abuse is higher with short- and long-acting oxycodone, known as Percodan (oxycodone with aspirin) and Percocet (oxycodone with acetaminophen).[6] Notably, the new guidelines issued by the Center for Disease Control and Prevention (CDC) in March 2016 specifically *exempted* patients with active cancer and those undergoing palliative care and end-of-life care from prescribing restrictions, recognizing that patients in these groups have pain that is appropriately treated with opioid pain medication, with a low risk of addiction.[7]

Another worry for end-of-life pain relief is drug/opioid tolerance. Addiction is distinct from tolerance, which is a physiological state of adaptation whereby the dosages of an opiate need to be increased to achieve the same pain-relief result; this tolerance often occurs in a person who takes opioids for more than a few days. Because of it, there is no upper limit on the amount of morphine that can be used; so, extremely large doses can be used safely if the drug is adjusted properly and the person is able to tolerate any side effects. Escalating pain, requiring higher dosing of pain medicine, is often a sign of worsening of the terminal illness. Tolerance is different from dependence, which produces harmful withdrawal symptoms if the drug is abruptly discontinued. Tolerance is also clearly not addiction, which is characterized by compulsive drug use and cravings.[8]

Constipation is the most common side effect of opioids, affecting up to 87% of terminally ill patients who receive them. This is why a bowel

4. http://www.ncbi.nlm.nih.gov/pubmed/22014206.
5. http://www.aafp.org/afp/2000/0201/p755.html.
6. Quill, et al. *Primer of Palliative Care,* 6th ed., 2014, p. 33.
7. http://www.cdc.gov/mmwr/volumes/65/rr/rr6501e1.htm.
8. Quill, et al. *Primer of Palliative Care,* 6th Ed, 2014, p. 33.

regimen (laxatives and stool softeners) must be routinely prescribed for the terminally ill person on opioid pain relievers.[9]

Another important consideration in end-of-life pain management with morphine is the phenomenon known as the *first-pass effect*. Oral morphine is one of several drugs that has a significant first-pass effect, whereby the concentration of the dose is greatly reduced as it is absorbed through the stomach and then metabolized by the liver. The bioavailability—the amount of drug ultimately available in the circulation—is reduced by the first-pass effect. With morphine, roughly two-thirds of an oral dose is removed by the liver through the first-pass effect. However, when given in an injection, 100% of the morphine dose is bioavailable to provide pain relief. The first-pass effect must be taken into account to achieve good pain control.[10]

Questions you may want to ask of the health-care provider managing pain:

- Has the doctor had special training in pain management?
- What are the options for controlling pain?
- Are any alternative therapies used, such as massage or acupuncture?
- Are any advanced therapies used, such as nerve blocks or injections?
- What side effects can be expected from the pain medication?
- Are there any pain control options that allow one to stay alert?
- What can be done if pain suddenly escalates?

Here are some sources for readers wanting more detailed information:

- Pharmacologic Management of Pain at the End of Life from *American Family Physician*: http://www.aafp.org/afp/2014/0701/p26.html

9. http://www.ncbi.nlm.nih.gov/pubmed/22014206.
10. http://tmedweb.tulane.edu/pharmwiki/doku.php/bioavailability_the_first_pass_effect.

- Pain Management in the Elderly at the End of Life from *The North American Journal of Medical Science*: http://www.ncbi.nlm.nih.gov/pmc/articles/PMC3234146/
- Pain Management in End of Life Care from *The Journal of the American Osteopathic Association*: http://jaoa.org/article.aspx?articleid=2093056
- Primer of Palliative Care, 6th Edition, from the American Academy of Hospice and Palliative Medicine

Acknowledgments

PUTTING THE DETAILS of this nightmarish experience in writing was extraordinarily difficult.

I am grateful to Bob Weiss, who was in the audience for my first attempt at public speaking. He mentored me as I worked on my speaking skills. Bob also actively encouraged me to put my story in writing. He graciously and generously donated his time and expertise in helping me launch this effort.

Matt Zencey provided extensive assistance in writing and editing, massaging style and shaping the narrative of my story. A talented and witty writer and editor, he expertly dissected my 400-plus pages of manuscript to a readable version half that size. He provided invaluable insight, advice, and encouragement, and I was fortunate to have him as my advisor, editor, and friend. I appreciate all he has done to help me with this endeavor.

Jennifer Cappello, senior editor at Sunbury Press, provided helpful suggestions and expert editing to this book.

I am grateful to all who took the time to read and comment on my manuscript. You have my heartfelt thanks.

I sincerely thank everyone who stood by me—family, friends, co-workers, neighbors, advocates, and strangers—during the worst experience of my life. My mother, my husband, my children, and many other family members endured the pain and trauma along with me, and were steadfast in their support and love. For all of this, I will be eternally grateful.

About the Author

BARBARA MANCINI graduated from Penn State University and Widener University with degrees in nursing. She has worked in emergency nursing for over three decades.

In 2013, she was arrested and prosecuted in Pennsylvania on the charge of aiding the attempted suicide of her dying 93-year old father after handing him his prescribed morphine five days before his death. A hospice nurse and police ignored his written advanced directives, and he was then hospitalized and treated in defiance of his end-of-life wishes. Barbara's prosecution lasted a year, during which time it garnered national and global attention, and it was roundly criticized throughout the media.

She has traveled the country speaking about her experience, and has become a vocal advocate for improved end-of-life care and expanded end-of-life options. Her criminal case also led to her interest in criminal justice advocacy, and in 2017 she completed an internship with the Pennsylvania Innocence Project. She began work as a paralegal in the pre-trial unit of the Montgomery County Public Defender's Office in 2018.

She lives in Philadelphia with her family.

Made in the USA
Columbia, SC
16 January 2020